RECOLLECTIONS
OF DEATH

RECOLLECTIONS OF DEATH

A Medical Investigation

MICHAEL B. SABOM, M.D., F.A.C.C.

1817

HARPER & ROW, PUBLISHERS, New York
Cambridge, Philadelphia, San Francisco,
London, Mexico City, São Paulo, Sydney

To Claire Diane, with love

Designer: Robin Malkin

Library of Congress Cataloging in Publication Data

Sabom, Michael B.
    Recollections of death.
    Includes index.
    1. Death, Apparent. 2. Death (Biology) I. Title.
QP87.S2   1982   616.07'8   81–47236
        ISBN 0–06–014895–0   AACR2

82 83 84 85 10 9 8 7 6 5 4 3 2

Contents

Acknowledgments		vii
Preface		xi
1.	Beginnings	1
2.	General Characteristics of the Near-Death Experience	14
3.	The Autoscopic Near-Death Experience	24
4.	The Transcendental Near-Death Experience	39
5.	Analysis of the Data	55
6.	Surgical Experiences	63
7.	The Autoscopic Near-Death Experience: Fact or Fantasy?	80
8.	"Afterexperiences": Recurrent Autoscopic Encounters	116
9.	Implications of the Near-Death Experience	124
10.	Explanations	151
11.	Thoughts on the Meaning of the Near-Death Experience	179
	Appendix	187
	References	214
	Index	219

Acknowledgments

I AM DEEPLY INDEBTED to many individuals for their assistance in conducting this study and in preparing this book—to the doctors and nurses at the University of Florida and at the Atlanta Veterans Administration Medical Center for referring patients who had survived a near-death crisis; to Dr. Kenneth Ring, Dr. Raymond Moody, Jr., and John Audette for boundless encouragement and support; to John Egle, publisher of Mockingbird Books, for his guidance with the publication of this book; to my brother, Dr. Steve Sabom, for his critique of the manuscript; to Jeanne Flagg of Harper & Row for her editorial assistance; and to Lani Shaw for typing the manuscript.

I am particularly indebted to Sarah Kreutziger, who introduced me to this subject and who worked with me on the study during its early years. Sarah helped design the format of this investigation and interviewed several of the patients whose accounts are found here.

Finally, I wish to thank Diane, my wife, for the long and stimulating hours we spent discussing the near-death experience, for her major reworkings of early drafts of the manuscript, and above all, for her steady encouragement to continue the study and to publish the book.

There are some odd things about human dying, anyway, that don't fit at all with the notion of agony at the end. People who almost die but don't, and then recover to describe the experience, never mention anguish or pain, or even despair; to the contrary they recall a strange, unfamiliar feeling of tranquility and peace. The act of dying seems to be associated with some other event, perhaps pharmacologic, that transforms it into something quite different from what most of us are brought up to anticipate. We might be learning more about this . . . Something is probably going on that we don't yet know about.

LEWIS THOMAS, M.D.
President, Sloan-Kettering Cancer Institute
New England Journal of Medicine
June 1977

Preface

OVER THE CENTURIES, a variety of experiences have been recounted by people who have almost died. A brilliant light, a beautiful landscape, the spirits of long-departed loved ones, all have figured in what were referred to as visions of death. Relatives gathered around the dying person to say their goodbyes, to hear his last words. If the person miraculously recovered, he might recall a floating sensation, then a "coming back."

Now more than ever before, people are returning from the threshold of death. Because of recent advances in medical technology, hearts can be restarted, breathing restored, blood pressure sustained. Patients who in the not so distant past would surely have died are now being brought back to continue their earthly existence. They are remembering more of their experiences, and we are listening. "If one considers death as a continuum or as a process," says Dr. George E. Burch,* the esteemed cardiologist, "then certainly these patients who have been resuscitated after several minutes of absent heart action have experienced and retrieved psychic information from as deep within this continuum as is possible. . . . The introduction of effective methods of cardiac resuscita-

*Professor of Medicine, Tulane University; Past President of the American College of Cardiology and editor of the *American Heart Journal.*

tion . . . has placed the physician in the unique position of being able to explore the associated psychic experiences with dying and death."[1]

In my own practice of cardiology over the past five years, I have conducted an extensive investigation into the experiences encountered by persons who have been very close to death. Many of these people, victims of cardiac arrest and other life-threatening crises, recalled a series of extraordinary events that "took place" while they were unconscious and near death. Some considered this experience to be a privileged glimpse of another realm of existence.

This book explores the nature and meaning of the near-death experience. My aim is not to repeat what has already been said on the subject or to offer new anecdotes for their own sake, but to present fresh observations on the content of the experience, on the people who encounter it, and on the clinical setting in which it occurs. In the light of these observations, I then reexamine the various explanations of the near-death experience that have appeared in scientific journals and in the popular press. The recollections of dying that fill these pages should in turn take on new significance.

What I learned at the bedside and in the clinic during this study has led me to rethink some of my own basic beliefs concerning the nature of man, the process of dying, and the practice of medicine. I present my findings to you in the hope that you will share in the awe and fascination that I have experienced while delving into these issues—issues that touch upon the very essence and meaning of life.

M.B.S.

Decatur, Georgia
March 1981

1

Beginnings

IN JULY 1970, I was beginning my medical internship at the University of Florida. My first night on call found me covering the medical floor in the main hospital and backing up another intern assigned to the emergency room. My early-evening hours were spent with routine duties— taking histories and performing physicals on three elective admissions, restarting IVs, and running an electrocardiogram on a patient with chest pain. At midnight, I lay down to read the latest issue of a medical journal and fell instantly asleep. At 3:15 A.M. I was jolted awake by a "stat" page: "Code 99, Emergency Room, first floor . . . Code 99, Emergency Room, first floor." I bolted down the stairs.

So began a ritual which I have repeated countless times. As you might have guessed, "Code 99" is medical shorthand for a patient in "extreme distress." It is the familiar call for help which summons doctors and nurses to the bedside of a patient whose condition has taken a dramatic turn for the worse. In essence, it identifies the condition of a patient *near death.*

At this point in my life, and for some years after, I was too busy with the routine requirements of my medical training to give much thought to what death would be like. I was being trained to keep people alive; it was not for me to contemplate the fate of those who didn't make it. I suppose if someone had asked me what I thought of death, I would have said that with death you are dead and that is the end of it. Although I had been raised in a churchgoing family, I had always tried to keep religious and scientific doctrines separate. For me at the time, Christian beliefs in life after death served the purpose of guiding proper worldly behavior and of relieving anxieties about death and dying, but such teachings remained subjective and unscientific.

Unscientific—that I would never be. Years of medical training had convinced me that if one pursued the scientific method—using laboratory protocol and research—most, if not all, of the unanswered questions of the universe would eventually be answered in one form or another. There were thus no such things as inexplicable phenomena, but merely "scientific facts" waiting to be discovered. Design the proper scientific study and the answer would be found.

As every student who has ever taken a course in science knows, the scientific method of investigation is the systematic collection of objective observations known as "data." Only data collected and presented in a rigorous, unbiased manner, however, are eligible for admission into the generally accepted body of scientific knowledge. In medicine, the clinical application of such data-based knowledge has largely been responsible for modern advances in medical diagnosis and treatment. Moreover, the physician who can most effectively master and apply the known scientific data concerning a medical disease process will, in turn, have the best chance of successfully treating such a disease when it appears in a patient.

Early on in medical school, I strongly embraced this basic logic of the scientific method in relation to the diagnosis and treatment of disease. I became particularly attracted to those aspects of medicine which dealt with the collection and utilization of measurable physiologic data. Thus, in the later years of my training, I was drawn to the subspecialty of cardiology—a precise technological discipline which relies heavily on the recording and interpretation of physiologic data and their application to cardiac disease and dysfunction. With the tools available to the modern cardiologist, diseases of the heart are like a puzzle, the pieces of which include the measured pressures within the four cardiac chambers, the mathematical formulas that utilize these pressures to compute cardiac function, and the specialized X-ray techniques that permit anatomic description of the cardiac disease. Moreover, I had come to accept that valid statements regarding all natural phenomena begin with the careful collection of pertinent data, from which conclusions or speculations can later be drawn.

In 1976, I was completing my first year of cardiology at the University of Florida in Gainesville. I was deeply involved in learning the nuances of clinical cardiology and was developing a preference for certain research pursuits in the field. At the same time, my wife and I had joined a local Methodist church. One Sunday morning that spring, Sarah Kreutziger, a psychiatric social worker at the university, presented at our adult Sunday school class a book that had caught her eye. The book, *Life After Life* by Dr. Raymond Moody, dealt with some strange experiences reported by people who had come close to death. Great interest was expressed by other members of the class. My own reaction, however, was less than enthusiastic. My indoctrinated scientific mind just couldn't relate seriously to these "far-out" descriptions of afterlife spirits and such. Being the only physician present that morning, I was asked for my opinion at the end of the class. The kindest thing I could find to say at the moment was "I don't believe it."

Later that week, Sarah phoned me. She had accepted an invitation to present Moody's book to a church-wide audience and wanted me to participate in the program as a medical consultant. I told her again how skeptical I was of Moody's findings, but she insisted that my part in the program would largely be to field the medical questions that were bound to come up with a topic of this sort. Somewhat reluctantly, I agreed.

In preparation for our talk, Sarah loaned me her copy of *Life After Life,* as the book had just come out and was not available in Gainesville bookstores. I studied it from cover to cover but remained unconvinced that it was nonfiction material. Shortly thereafter, Sarah and I met to plan the presentation. To add substance to the talk, we decided to conduct a brief survey of several of our own hospitalized patients who had survived a medical crisis similar to those in Moody's book. We would ask them if *they* had had any experiences while unconscious and near death. If none had had such an experience (as I fully expected), then at least we could report to our audience that indeed "We asked." If, by some chance, an experience was described, then this could be used as a substantive example for our presentation.

Finding patients who had survived a medical crisis would be a simple matter for both Sarah and me. She had daily contact with patients in the kidney dialysis unit. Many of them had had more than one near-death encounter during their long course of kidney failure, which now required in-hospital dialysis. I, on the other hand, was caring for a variety of patients who had been resuscitated from cardiac arrest. We began our interviewing.

The third patient I approached was a middle-aged housewife from Tampa who, by her medical records, had suffered several near-death crisis events of various sorts. She was in the hospital for routine diagnostic tests. I met her in her room one evening about eight o'clock and we had a lengthy discussion about the medical details of her previous illnesses. Finally, I asked her if she had had any experiences during the times she was unconscious and critically ill. As soon as she was convinced that I was not an underground psychiatrist posing as a cardiologist, she began describing the first near-death experience I had heard in my medical career. To my utter amazement, the details matched the descriptions in *Life After Life*. I was even more impressed by her sincerity and the deep personal significance her experience had had for her. At the conclusion of the interview, I had the distinct feeling that what this woman had shared with me that night was a deeply personal glimpse into an aspect of medicine of which I knew nothing.

Early the next day, I informed Sarah of my finding. She had similar news to report—hers from a patient with chronic liver and kidney failure. We decided to tape-record these accounts for our upcoming presentation. Both our patients agreed to have their experiences recorded as long as their identities would not be disclosed.

Our presentation of *Life After Life* with the tape-recorded experiences of our two patients was enthusiastically received by an overflowing church-wide audience. To me this simply meant that my obligation to Sarah had been more than met. Still, over the next few weeks, I thought often of the woman I had interviewed and of the effect the experience had had on her subsequent life. In medical terms, she had been quite lucky to survive her close brushes with death. But more important to her than the fact of her survival was the experience she had had when unconscious and near death. I pondered the significance in all this for me.

I returned to Moody's book. Several things continued to bother me about his material and his method of presentation. For one thing, the cases in *Life After Life* had been collected in a very casual, unsystematic manner. Many of the reports were from people who had approached Moody with their experiences following one of his presentations on the subject. There was no way of telling whether such testimonies were authentic or were merely fabricated replays. Moreover, Moody stated that 150 persons had been interviewed for his book, but only a small fraction of this number were included in it as examples. Did the experiences of all 150 people fit nicely into the patterns he described or were these basic patterns of the near-death experience based upon a selected minority of the overall group, which was unrepresentative of the experience in general? Who were the people who reported these experiences and what were their social, educational, professional and religious backgrounds? And most of all, as a physician I wanted to know the medical details of the crisis events that purportedly had led to the near-death experiences. I was troubled by these exclusions from his book. Moody himself acknowledged many of the pitfalls of his work in the disclaimer at the end of *Life After Life*: "In writing this book I have been acutely conscious that my purpose and perspectives might very easily be misunderstood. In particular, I would like to say to scientifically-minded readers that I am fully aware that what I have done here does not constitute a scientific study."

To answer my questions, a "scientific study" would have to be conducted. I decided to give it a try. I contacted Sarah and she was receptive. From our initial interviewing experience we had realized that with our immediate access to a wide variety of patients with life-threatening illnesses, we were both in ideal positions to carry out such an investigation. We were actively involved in either the treatment or the counseling of these patients, and we needed no special clearance to contact them directly for interviews. Moreover, we were identified by both patients and staff as primary members of the medical team, and not as outside researchers who had suddenly appeared on the scene for some out-of-the-ordinary purpose.

I reviewed with Sarah my major objections to Moody's work, and from this we devised our study, based on six questions that we wanted to answer. First, we wanted to confirm that these near-death experiences were really occurring in patients while they were critically ill and near death. We were encouraged by having already found two cases, but we needed many more before we could be confident that a consistent experience was indeed taking place. Our initial idea was to interview twenty or thirty patients and then to publish our findings as a preliminary report in a medical journal.

Second, we wanted to examine carefully the content of personally collected cases and compare our findings with Moody's anecdotal descriptions of the near-death experience in *Life After Life*.[1] Did these experiences follow a consistent pattern or did they vary significantly from person to person?

Third, how common is the near-death experience? To answer this question, a group of near-death survivors would have to be interviewed without Sarah's or my knowing beforehand whether or not a near-death experience had been encountered. The frequency of occurrence of the near-death experience could then be determined by comparing the number of persons reporting a near-death experience with the total number of near-death survivors interviewed. Such an approach is known as a *prospective* study.

Fourth, what were the educational, occupational, social and religious backgrounds of persons reporting such an experience at the point of death. Would this information provide clues as to why some people encountered a near-death experience and others did not? Furthermore, did medical matters such as the type of near-death crisis event, the duration of unconsciousness or the method of resuscitation influence the occurrence of the near-death experience?

Fifth, was the content of the near-death experience influenced in some way by the person's background characteristics or the medical details of the near-death crisis event? For instance, did only the devoutly religious describe a being of light and a beautiful afterworld environment? Could plausible out-of-body descriptions of the techniques of resuscitation be given only by well-educated, informed individuals who had some knowledge of such procedures from their reading, from lay courses in cardiopulmonary resuscitation (CPR) or the like? Did only persons unconscious for long periods of time encounter the "afterworld"?

Finally, was the reduction in death fears expressed by the people interviewed by Moody a result of the near-death experience per se, or merely the result of having survived a close brush with death?

A further thought had plagued me ever since I read Moody's book. Moody noted that many people had later been able to recall specific events that transpired in the vicinity of their physical body at a time when they were presumed to be unconscious. More important, this recall had consisted of visual details. Moody did not attempt to substantiate these reports by medical records or other available sources, however. Now, the majority of patients whom I would be interviewing had been resuscitated from a cardiac arrest. By this time in my career, I had personally directed and participated in well over a hundred such resuscitations. I knew what a resuscitation consisted of, that is, how it would look. I was anxiously awaiting the moment when a patient would claim that he had "seen" what had transpired in his room during his own resuscitation. Upon such an encounter, I intended to probe meticulously for details that would not ordinarily be known to nonmedical personnel. In essence, I would pit my experience as a trained cardiologist against the professed visual recollections of lay individuals. In so doing, I was convinced that obvious inconsistencies would appear which would reduce these purported visual observations to no more than an "educated guess" on the part of the patient.

Having decided on the objectives for our study, Sarah and I discussed the criteria for patient selection. Because of the highly subjective nature of the material, we decided to exclude any patients with a known psychiatric illness or significant mental impairment from any cause. At the very least, we needed assurance that our subjects were mentally competent before their testimony could be accepted into our study. Aside from this one exclusionary provision, any patient who had suffered a near-death crisis event (see below) would be eligible for interview. I would be responsible for contacting patients who had survived a near-death crisis in the medical intensive care units of the two University of Florida hospitals—Shands and Veterans Administration. Sarah would survey cases admitted to the kidney dialysis units of Shands and cases she encountered on her general consultative rounds with critically ill individuals.

As for the crisis event itself, it would include any illness or episode in which the patient had been rendered unconscious and physically near death. But what was to be our definition of unconsciousness and how was this to be determined? I pondered this question because no generally acceptable medical or scientific definition of unconsciousness had been proposed which could consistently be verified using objective scientific techniques. Anesthesiologists, using all the clinical skills and technology (including electroencephalography) at their disposal, are often unable to determine accurately the level of awareness (or consciousness) of closely monitored patients under general anesthesia.[2] Numerous reports in the medical literature have described patients who, presumed to be under deep surgical anesthesia, could later recall intense pain and fright while lying on the operating table partially awake.[3] Likewise, psychologists and physiologists in nonclinical situations have had equal difficulty in clearly defining the human state of unconsciousness. For purposes of our study, however, we decided to use the term "unconsciousness" to denote any specific period of time during which the person lost all subjective awareness of environment and self. In lay terms, this is most commonly referred to as "blacking out."

In addition to unconsciousness, each patient must have been physically "near death." You may ask if this would be the same as "clinical death." Unfortunately, the term "clinical death" has been so indiscriminately used in recent years that it has lost precise meaning. Years ago, Professor Negovskii, a Russian scientist, defined the term on the basis of a series of physiologic experiments conducted at the Laboratory of Experimental Physiology of Resuscitation at the Academy of Medical Sciences in the U.S.S.R. Employing an experimental model of severe lethal blood loss in dogs, he defined "clinical death" as follows:

> Clinical death is a state during which all external signs of life (consciousness, reflexes, respiration and cardiac activity) are absent, but the organism as a whole is not yet dead; the metabolic processes of its tissues still proceed and under definite conditions it is possible to restore all its functions; i.e., this state is reversible under appropriate therapeutic intervention. If the organism in a state of clinical death is allowed to take the natural course of events, then the state of clinical death is followed by an irreversible state—biological death. The transition from the states of clinical death to biological death is simultaneously a break and a continuous process, because in its initial stages it is already impossible to completely restore the activity of the organism in all its functions, including those of the central nervous system, but it is still possible to restore the organism with altered functions of the brain cortex, i.e., an organism which cannot function under natural conditions of existence. Thereafter it becomes possible to restore under artificial conditions the activity of only certain organs, and further on, even this becomes no longer possible. During biological death, metabolic activity degradation, specific for a dead organism, sets in. . . . Considerable experimental material gathered by several authors indicates that 5–6 minutes is the maximum duration of the state of clinical death which the brain cortex of an adult organism can survive with subsequent recovery of all its functions.[4]

Clinical death as defined by this Russian scientist is a precise description of a specific physiologic state. Today, this term has been used to describe a wide variety of medical and nonmedical conditions: the cardiac arrest victim with absent heartbeat and respiration, the comatose patient with persisting heartbeat and respiration, the person found "unresponsive" on the street corner from a simple uncomplicated faint or alcoholic stupor, and so on. To compound this problem, "brain death" is now a popular medical term used to denote irreversible, generalized cerebral inactivity (i.e., "flat EEG") in a patient deemed medically irretrievable—even in the face of continuing cardiac activity. Using Negovskii's definition of clinical death, the "brain death" victim is not clinically dead because of persisting normal cardiac activity, but on the other hand, is often considered "dead enough" not to warrant medical life support measures. Because of this obvious confusion of terminology, we elected to select patients we termed physically near death—that is, in any bodily state resulting from an extreme physiological catastrophe, accidental or otherwise, that would reasonably be expected to result in irreversible biological death in the majority of instances and would demand urgent medical attention, if available. In general, these conditions would include cardiac arrest, severe traumatic injury, deep comatose situations from a metabolic derangement or systemic illness, and the like.

As it turned out, a few persons in this study came so near death that they had actually been given up for dead. A striking example of this is the case of an American soldier (Interview 69, Table I) who received multiple battlefield injuries early one morning in Vietnam. So badly mangled was his body that he was assumed to be dead by everyone who had anything to do with him: (1) the North Vietnamese soldiers who stripped him of his boots and pistol belt; (2) the American soldiers who placed his body in a bag and deposited it on a truck with other corpses; and (3) a mortician who cut into his left groin looking for a vein in which to inject embalming fluid. The oozing of blood from the mortician's incision was the first clue that this man was not yet dead.

Our interviewing methods were standardized to minimize any bias we might impart into the verbal descriptions of our interviewed patients. When initially approaching the patient, we would avoid mentioning our interest in the near-death experience and would act as if only routine medical details were being sought. The patient would be asked to reconstruct the events that could be remembered immediately preceding the loss of consciousness and then to recall those immediately upon awakening. Inquiry would then be made about recollections from the period of unconsciousness.

As it turned out, the patients were totally unaware of the real intent of the interview until we asked about any experience while unconscious. At this point, some patients claimed to have no recollection and would merely restate the fact that they had been totally unconscious, blacked out and unaware of anything going on at the time. Other patients, however, would hesitate, look at us in a guarded manner and reply, "Why do you ask?" We would routinely give the following response: "I am interested in the experiences and reactions of patients who have survived critical medical illnesses. Some patients have indicated that they have experienced certain events while unconscious and quite ill. I am sincerely interested in any such experiences, no matter what they may be." Whereupon, such a patient would usually begin to unfold his near-death experience, prefacing his remarks with "You won't believe this, but . . . "; "I've never told anyone about this, but . . ."; "This sounds crazy, but . . ."; etc.

Once it was clear that the patient had had an experience while unconscious, we would ask permission to tape-record the balance of the interview. On rare occasions, the circumstances of the interview (e.g., the noisy hospital environment found in an open-ward intensive care unit) would preclude the judicious use of a tape recorder, and extensive notes would be taken to document, as much as possible, the experience in the patient's own words. The telling of the near-death experience could then proceed without further interruption from us. Once the patient had described his experience in its entirety, we would question him about details that needed clarification. Our goal was to gather enough information about each experience so that it could later be evaluated on the basis of ten separate elements which had been derived from Moody's description of the experience in *Life After Life*. These ten elements were:

1. *Subjective sense of being dead.* Did the patient describe the experience as if he had died or was some other interpretation given? How did the near-death experience compare to individual dreams or to drug-induced hallucinations the patient may have encountered from medicinal narcotics received for prior illnesses?

2. *Predominant emotional content.* Did the patient feel calm and/or peaceful, frightened and/or upset, or feel no emotions during the near-death experience? In particular, if the physical body was "viewed" in the throes of a resuscitation, was this a frightening and painful experience?

3. *Sense of bodily separation.* Did the patient describe the sensation of being separated from his physical body during the near-death experience? If so, how was this "separated self" perceived?

4. *Observation of physical objects and events.* Did the patient claim to have seen and/or heard what was going on in the room during the period of physical unconsciousness? If so, were these observations perceived from the physical body or from a point separate from the physical body? What were the specific details of these observations?

5. *Dark region or void.* Did the patient perceive a passage into a dark region or void at some point during the near-death experience?

6. *Life review.* Did the patient perceive a rapid replay of previous life events? If so, how did this replay take place and what was the nature of the recalled events?

7. *A light.* Did the patient perceive the presence of a brilliant

source of light, and if so, was some meaning or identification attached to this light?

8. *Entering a transcendental environment.* Did the patient perceive another region or dimension apart from the surroundings of his physical body and the dark region or void? What was the nature of such an environment? Did it contain a border or limit which represented to them, as to Moody's cases, the "point of no return" to the physical body?

9. *Encountering others.* Did the patient either *feel* or *see* the presence of other "spirits" during the near-death experience? If so, how were these "spiritual beings" identified? Were they known to be dead or alive at the time, and was there any communication between the patient and these other personages? If so, what were the nature and content of any such communication?

10. *Return.* Did the patient perceive his "return" from near death as a voluntary, involuntary or spontaneous occurrence? Was there an assigned reason for the return?

The structured portion of the interview would end with the brief collection of certain biographical items: age, sex, race, years of formal education, occupation, place of residence, religious affiliation and frequency of church attendance. We would also inquire as to whether the patient was aware of the near-death experience from other sources prior to his own near-death encounter. Finally, each patient would be asked to evaluate the effect, if any, that the crisis event (with or without a near-death experience) had had on his fear of dying and on his belief in an afterlife.

At the completion of the interview, we would allow time for each patient to discuss any questions or feelings he might have. As it turned out, almost every patient who had had a near-death experience, in one way or another, expressed deep gratitude to us for having taken the time and interest to listen to his experience. Many had been unable to discuss it with their closest friends or relatives for fear of ridicule and thus had found it reassuring that Sarah or I had listened in an uncritical manner.

The timing of the interview was significant. If the patient had recently undergone a near-death crisis, we wanted to interview him as soon after the event as possible, while the details were fresh in his mind. Moreover, an early interview would minimize the possibility that the content of the patient's experience had been influenced by discussions with family members, by reading materials on the subject and so forth. The medical condition of the patient had to be relatively stable, however, before we thought it appropriate to initiate our interview. The retelling of the near-death experience was likely to be a very emotional event which could have untoward effects on a critically ill and unstable patient.

The location of the interview would depend on the medical condition of the patient. Our goal was to create as private and uninterrupted an atmosphere as possible for our interviewing and tape recording. If the patient was ambulatory, the interview would be conducted in the most available private hospital room or office. Many interviews would of necessity be conducted at bedside. Recording was to be done on the spot and would sometimes have to be interrupted for the steady stream of clinical procedures associated with typical hospital routine (administration of medication, blood pressure checks, etc.). Occasionally, a patient's debility would necessitate the interview's being broken off entirely and continued the next day. At the onset, Sarah and I recognized that in dealing with hospitalized patients recovering from a near-fatal event, a lengthy interview would not be practical. Accordingly, we limited our background questioning to a few essential items and focused our main efforts on the content of the near-death experience itself.

Our interviewing began in earnest in May 1976. In time, other physicians and paramedical personnel learned of our research and began referring to us their patients who had had a near-death experience. Furthermore, we began giving talks to local churches and civic groups and invariably would pick up a few new cases from the audience. We interviewed these persons, too, and made every effort to obtain their medical records to document the details of their crisis events. Since these cases came to our attention *because* the person had had a near-death experience, they did not fit with the design of a prospective study, as described earlier in this chapter. Many of the questions we wanted answered about the near-death experience (e.g., frequency of occurrence) required a prospective approach. Thus, in the analysis of our data, these referred cases were kept strictly separate from the prospective, in-hospital interviews. When the prospective and referred cases are drawn on later in this book to describe various aspects of the near-death experience, each is so labeled, using an Interview number keyed to Table I in the Appendix.

As the interviewing progressed, it became obvious that patients who had had a near-death experience during their crisis event had lost much of their fear of dying, a result that was not being reported by patients who had survived similar crisis events without such an experience. We decided to document further this apparent difference in death attitudes between patients with and without a near-death experience by mailing each person in the study two death anxiety scales—the Templer[5] and the Dickstein.[6] These scales had been separately validated through published reports in the psychological literature. The scales were mailed to each patient at least six months after the date of interview.

In July 1978, I completed my training at Florida and moved to Atlanta to assume my present position as assistant professor of medicine at Emory University School of Medicine and as staff physician at the Atlanta Veterans Administration Medical Center. Sarah has moved to Louisiana to complete her doctoral studies in social work. My position at Emory and the Veterans Administration Hospital has increased my accessibility to near-death survivors, for I'm in daily contact with patients on the general medical wards and in the intensive-care units. Moreover, physicians and paramedical personnel at other hospitals in Atlanta are referring to me their patients who have reported a near-death experience. Thus my study is continuing. This book represents a compilation of the data collected during five years of investigation—from May 1976 through March 1981.

2

General Characteristics of the Near-Death Experience

IN AUGUST 1977, a 60-year-old white male security guard was hospitalized with a history of progressive weakness and somnolence. Shortly after admission, he was diagnosed as having acute intermittent porphyria, a rare, severe, metabolic disorder associated with the Guillian-Barré Syndrome (a paralyzing neurological disorder of uncertain etiology). His condition deteriorated rapidly and he was moved to the medical intensive care unit on the twenty-ninth of August. Despite all medical efforts, the man became comatose and unresponsive on September 2. His blood pressure required support with intravenous medications. His respiration was completely controlled with a ventilator set on automatic cycle. His eyes were taped shut to avoid corneal ulceration from continued exposure to the air (he couldn't close his eyelids). Four days later, his condition had not improved. An electroencephalogram was performed to determine if the life-support measures should be continued. The report came back: "Severely abnormal EEG with diffuse slow-wave activity"—that is, some brain-wave activity could still be detected. Life-support measures were maintained. On September 10, the man began showing some response to painful stimuli and the coma started to lift. Thirty-four days later, he was transferred out of the intensive care unit, after having survived episodes of complete kidney failure, gastrointestinal hemorrhage requiring several blood transfusions, and recurrent pneumonia. On November 1, 1977, I interviewed him in his room about his recent period of unconsciousness. He was unable to speak in more than a whisper because of injury to his vocal cords from the recently removed endotracheal tube (inserted into the lungs through the mouth to permit respiration by an artificial ventilator). Yet with great intensity, he began his story:

> Anything that I tell you is actually what happened. It's very weird. I've read some pretty wild stories on this but I'm really sincere. . . . That's an experience I've never had before. It was so definite. . . . I think once you've penetrated *the big secret* just a bit like I did, it's enough to convince you. . . . If somebody questions me on this I am going to say, "Hey, look. This is it." (I–23)*

And then unfolded a remarkable experience during which this man "observed" a medical team working over his unconscious body. In this encounter, he felt he had been let in on "the big secret" to life and death. As we examine the near-death experiences (NDEs) described by this man and others in this study, a number of common characteristics emerge.

Ineffability

Most people who had encountered an NDE expressed great difficulty in finding the right words to describe their experience. In reviewing the tapes of our recorded interviews, we were struck by people's attempting to describe the "indescribable." Many tried to make comparisons between their NDE and dreams or other personal experiences, only to end up saying that such analogies were grossly inadequate. This ineffability of the NDE was typically expressed in the following ways: "I can't even explain it." (I–44); "There is no feeling you experience in normal life that is anything like this." (I–3)

Sense of Timelessness

All persons described their NDE as if it had occurred in a timeless dimension. As events were being perceived during the experience, all

---

* Interview number 23. For a complete listing of interviews, see Appendix, Table I. To preserve anonymity, the names and hospital numbers of all persons interviewed have been omitted. Initials used to designate persons in the text do not correspond to real names. Exact dates of hospital admissions have not been given.

intuitive sense of the duration of the experience was lost. Thus: "You're like in a state of suspended animation." (I–53); "I can't pinpoint time in a situation like that. It might have been a minute." (I–23); "There was no measurement of time. I don't know if it was a minute or five or ten hours." (I–3)

Sense of Reality

A profound sense of reality pervaded the experience, both while it was happening and later, in its recollection. Most persons emphasized at least once during the interview that their NDE was real, "as real as you and I sitting here talking at this moment," as one person put it. Typical of this emphasis on the reality of the experience are these comments: "It's reality. I know for myself that I didn't experience no fantasy. There was no so-called dream or nothing. These things really happened to me. It happened. I know. I went through it." (I–15); "I was looking down from the ceiling and there were no ifs, ands or buts about it." (I–14); "That was real. If you want to, I'm perfectly willing for you to give me Sodium Pentothal. . . . It's real as hell." (I–19); "I *know* it was real. I *know* that I was up there. I *know* that. And I *know* that I seen me down there. I could swear on a Bible that I was there. I seen things just like I see them now." (I–63–2)*

One man even felt that his NDE was "realer than here, really. After that the world seemed like a mockery to real life—make-believe. Like people playing games. Like we're getting prepared for something but we don't know what." (I–5)

Sense of Death

The NDE was interpreted by almost every person as a "death experience"—that is, they thought they had died or were dying. This sense of death was a strong intuitive feeling that came early in the experience. In many cases, physical unconsciousness was a sudden and unexpected occurrence, such as with a stoppage of the heart. In the NDE, the feeling of "death" purportedly unfolded without allowing time for the person to *consciously* anticipate the nearness of death prior to loss of consciousness. One 45-year-old survivor of an unexpected cardiac arrest in a small community hospital in southern Georgia told me that the first thing he

* When a person reported more than one NDE, the interview ("I") number consists of both the number of the interview (i.e., "63") and the number denoting the particular NDE (i.e., "2") from which the passage is excerpted.

realized after losing consciousness was that "something funny was going on." I asked him what he meant by this and he replied: "I realized that I was dead . . . that I had died. [I thought,] I don't know whether the doctor knows it or not, but I know it." (I–60) He then went on to describe his NDE.

Another survivor of a sudden cardiac arrest, in the emergency room of a New York hospital, put it this way: "But I remember saying, 'I'm dying. I know I'm dying. Why are people so afraid of dying? Why? This is beautiful!' " (I–13)

The "experience of death" was likewise reported as being very real to a 46-year-old Georgia resident who suddenly lost consciousness during a cardiac arrest in 1969 and encountered an NDE: "I think I was dead for a while. I mean at least spirit-wise. I think my spirit left my body for a while. If that's death, it's not bad." (I–63–1)

In a few cases, a "death pronouncement" was recalled to have been made by someone else present during the near-death crisis event. One such instance was recounted by a 55-year-old woman from northern Florida who had suffered severe hemorrhagic shock after a major artery in her throat was accidentally severed during a tonsillectomy. Massive bleeding from her mouth and throat began after she had recovered from the surgical anesthesia and had been returned to her room. Her description of her near-death experience begins with the following observations:

> I was thinking to myself: What's wrong with me? Something is wrong, I know. And then, all of a sudden, I thought: Oh, I'm dying, that's what it is—and honestly, I was happy about it. I was really happy about dying. And then I heard her [a nurse] scream, "My God, she's gone. Oh, and she said she was just going to have her tonsils taken out and she's gone." (I–41)

It appears that this woman's awareness of "dying" preceded the nurse's declaration that indeed she was "gone."

Not all persons interpreted their NDE as a death experience. A 44-year-old ex–air force pilot who suffered a cardiac arrest in a military hospital in 1973 told me that during his resuscitation he felt "detached, standing off to the side and watching it all go on . . . an uninterested observer." When asked for his interpretation of this experience, he replied:

> Frankly, I just don't know. It's an unknown. It's something like a lot of things you don't necessarily believe in but you don't necessarily deny it. I don't know what did it, what caused it, or what the

phenomenon was. . . . Really, the only explanation I can have is that the brain still functions even though it's partially dead or starved from oxygen. Everybody believes you are out cold but you are still perceiving things even when you can't talk, or move.

A:* Visually perceive them?

S: Visually and audibly.

A: And visually perceive them from an aspect other than where you are lying?

S: Yes. It's like a dream. You're detached from the thing and watching it as a bystander.

A: But the things you are dreaming are really happening?

S: Oh, yes. They are real. . . . It's one of the facts of life you can't explain. (I–32)

This man was unsure of how to interpret his NDE, to him "one of the facts of life you can't explain."

Predominant Emotional Feelings

All persons reporting an NDE were asked to characterize their emotional feelings during the experience. What predominated was a feeling of calm, peace and/or tranquility in marked contrast to the physical pain and suffering experienced when the person was in a conscious physical state immediately prior to or following the NDE.

This contrast between the pain in the physical body and the painlessness during the NDE was emphasized by one 46-year-old man following his second cardiac arrest, in January 1978:

> [During the NDE] It was nice. It didn't hurt. In fact, no feeling at all whatsoever. I could see but I couldn't feel. . . . [After regaining consciousness] it hurt! . . . It didn't, say, hurt, but it burned. [The electric shock had] burned all the hair off my chest, with a blister here and here. (I–63–2)

Following a cardiac arrest in January 1979, a 55-year-old textile mill laborer recalled: "[After being resuscitated] I asked him [the doctor] why did he bring me back, as [during the NDE] I was never more peaceful in my life and [before] I had been having those horrible pains for so long." (I–66)

The pain from extensive head and internal injuries incurred as the

* A=Author; S=Subject.

result of an auto accident were seemingly "left behind" during the NDE of a 32-year-old ex-paratrooper. He described it as being "beautiful. No noise. Everything at peace. Everything just runs together." (I–4)

An auto-pedestrian accident left another man with multiple skull and leg fractures and a subsequent cardiac arrest. Referring to his NDE: "It is undescribable what you feel. It's really undescribable. It was so— so peaceful and restful. . . . Like I say, if I had my choice, I'd be back there. It's undescribable." (I–8)

An emergency "open-chest" heart operation was performed without anesthesia at the bedside of a 54-year-old patient at the Atlanta VA Medical Center. Immediately before the procedure, the man lost consciousness from profound shock (pericardial tamponade). Prior to unconsciousness, "it hurt so bad that it felt just like someone hitting you with a hammer every time your heart beat. Every beat was excruciating." Moments later, during the NDE:

> That was the most beautiful instant in the whole world when I came out of that body! . . . All I saw was extremely pleasant! I can't imagine anything in the world or out of the world that could anywhere compare. Even the most beautiful moments of life would not compare to what I was experiencing. (I–65)

However, periods of momentary sadness during the NDE were felt by some as they "viewed" the efforts of others to revive their lifeless physical body. A 37-year-old housewife from Florida recalled an episode of encephalitis or infection of the brain when she was four years old, during which she was unconscious and not expected to live. She remembers "looking down" on her mother from a point near the ceiling with the following feelings:

> The biggest thing that I remember was that I felt so *sad* that I couldn't somehow let her know that I was all right. Somehow I knew that I was all right, but I didn't know how to tell her. I just watched. . . . [But] it was a very calm, peaceful feeling. . . . In fact, it was a good feeling. (I–28–1)

Similar feelings were expressed by a 46-year-old man from north Georgia as he recounted his NDE during a cardiac arrest in January 1978: "I felt bad because my wife was crying and she seemed so helpless and all, you know. But it was nice. It didn't hurt." (I–63–2)

Sadness was recalled by a 73-year-old French teacher from Florida when she spoke of her NDE, which had occurred during a severe infectious illness and grand mal seizure at age fifteen:

> Then I became separated and I was sitting way up there looking at myself convulsing and my mother and my maid screaming and yelling because they thought I was dead. I felt so sorry for them and for my body.... Just deep, deep *sadness*. I can still feel the sadness. But I felt I was free up there and there was no reason for suffering. I had no pain and was completely free. (I–54–1)

One woman's otherwise happy NDE was interrupted by feelings of remorse at having to leave behind her children during a severe postoperative complication which had left her near death and physically unconscious: "Yes, yes, I was happy until I remembered the kids. Until then I seemed to be happy that I was dying. I really and truly was. It was just an elated feeling, a happy feeling." (I–41)

Feelings of loneliness and fright were sometimes recalled from the moment when the person felt thrust into a dark region or void during the NDE. Shortly following a nephrectomy (surgical removal of a kidney) at the University of Florida in 1976, a 23-year-old college student lost consciousness from an unexpected postoperative complication. During the initial portions of her NDE: "There was total blackness around me ... all you see is blackness around you. If you move very fast, you can feel the sides moving in on you.... I felt *lonely* and a little bit *frightened*." (I–29)

A similar darkness enveloped a 56-year-old man during a later portion of his NDE and "scared" him: "The next thing I remember, I was in complete total darkness.... It was a very dark place and I didn't know where I was, what I was doing there or what was happening, and I started getting *scared*." (I–8)

In each case in which unpleasant emotions (e.g., sadness, loneliness, fright) were encountered during the NDE, they were perceived to be but a momentary impression in an otherwise pleasant NDE, the overall content being later described as enjoyable. It is conceivable that this overall assessment might have been different (i.e., unenjoyable) if the experience had abruptly ended at the point at which the unpleasant emotion was perceived. Such was not the case with any of the persons interviewed in this study, however.

Separation from Physical Body

All persons in this study who related an NDE described it as if it had taken place outside their physical body. They felt the "essential" part of themselves had separated from the physical body, and that this part was able to perceive objects and events visually. During the NDE, the "separated self" became the sole "conscious" identity of the person, with the physical body remaining behind as an "empty shell." This dichotomy between the "separated self" and the unconscious physical body was described in the following manner by a 54-year-old Georgia construction worker following a cardiac arrest and an NDE in February 1976: "*I* recognized *me* laying there . . . about like looking at a dead worm or something. I didn't have any desire to go back to it." (I–65)

Ninety-three percent of persons perceived their "separated self" to be an invisible, nonmaterial entity. Such was the description given by a 48-year-old fireman from northern Florida who had lapsed into a deep uremic (kidney failure) coma at the University of Florida in 1977. During his NDE, while "separated" from his physical body, "There was no feeling of being, it was more like a spirit. . . . If you think about it, you can feel your clothes against your skin. But there was nothing there like that. There was no sensitive feeling as far as being." (I–53)

A similar description was given by an 84-year-old retired schoolteacher from Illinois, who had encountered an NDE during severe complications following a hysterectomy in the 1930s: "I was light, airy, and felt transparent." (I–46) She was so impressed with this experience at the time that she wrote the following poem to record this feeling:

> Hovering beneath the ceiling, I looked down
> Upon a body, untenanted—my own
> Strangely at peace, airy, weightless as light,
> I floated there, freed from pain-filled days and nights,
> Until a voice I heard, an urgent call,
> And again I dwelt within my body's wall.

Seven percent of persons described their "separated self" as if it had features consistent with their original physical body, but that these features were "visible" only to themselves. One 43-year-old man perceived his "separated self" to be clothed in a white robe during his NDE from a cardiac arrest in October 1976: "You feel like you're floating. I had a white robe on with a white belt which was interwoven and it had a tassel on both ends of it. . . . I had a white hood but I didn't have it up." (I–44)

Another survivor of a cardiac arrest somehow caught a "reflection" of himself in the midst of his NDE: "The next thing I remember was I was floating and I was a much younger man. . . . The impression I got was that I was able to see myself some way through a reflection or

something where I was twenty years younger than what I actually was."
(I-8)

During each of two separate near-death crisis events, several years
apart, a 60-year-old Ohio housewife encountered a different perception
of her "separated self":

[During the first NDE] I had a body, because my arms were up on
the arms of the chair. They just looked like arms. . . . [During the
second NDE] I don't know how to explain it. It's like I'm just, not
floating exactly, but I'm very light. Nothing that I had noticed other
than that I can see everything. . . . And I didn't have any sense of
breathing or anything like that. (I-45)

During the out-of-body episode, people would experience an amazing clarity of thought, as if they were alert and fully awake, not in their
physical body but in a "separated self." As a 51-year-old Florida resident who suffered a cardiac arrest said, referring to his "out-of-body"
experience: "Then the thought came to me, and it was a clear thought,
very clear, just the way I'm speaking to you now . . ." (I-3) Clear cognitive abilities were also described by a woman who experienced an "out-
of-body" state during a postoperative complication in 1952: "Your mind
is working, really and truly—well, it clicks as fast as mine is clicking
now. And that's the honest truth." (I-41) Yet another woman remarked
that during her NDE "I was fully in control of my mind." (I-46)

Insight into the nature of the unfolding events during the NDE was
also reported to have been preserved. During the experience itself, the
person often felt as if he was questioning or evaluating his own perception of the reality of the situation. Experientially, the perceptions were
apparently quite real, but rationally the existence of this reality was
often quite difficult to accept. In short, the question would be raised:
"How can this be?" Such was the case with a 23-year-old woman who,
while unconscious from a severe postoperative complication, perceived
the very "real" image of her deceased father during an NDE, though
"Even then my mind was saying, 'But I can't be seeing Daddy and
talking to him—he's dead' . . . yet I could see him perfectly." (I-29) Another man had similar difficulty in reconciling the reality of ongoing
events during his NDE with his own accepted norms of reality: "I remember saying, 'I don't know where I am or who can hear me,' and I
didn't know where I was because I was positive that I was looking at
something that was not happening to me and yet I knew it was me." (I-
3)

Insight into the unfolding events of the NDE was expressed somewhat differently by a 55-year-old public health nurse who became comatose for several days from a complication following a radical mastectomy in 1961: "The thing that I was conscious of was that I knew it was not a dream because I could hardly wait to get conscious so that I could tell my mother that I had seen my father." (I–37)

In this study, one of the more critically ill persons was a 54-year-old Illinois salesman who lapsed into a deep coma following a massive gastrointestinal hemorrhage, profound shock and (aspiration) pneumonia. At one point in his medical record, the treating physician had noted that this man "failed to respond even to painful stimuli." During this unconscious interval, he encountered an NDE in which he perceived himself to be "dying." At this point, the patient stated, "I had the power of thinking: Do I really want this to happen?" (I–52)

The "big secret" alluded to by the man interviewed at the beginning of this chapter is thus seen to unfold as an ineffable sense of timeless reality occurring apart from one's physical body and associated with a pleasant understanding of death. The next two chapters take a closer look at the stages of passage as the individual enters and goes deeper into the experience.

3

The Autoscopic
Near-Death Experience

NOVEMBER 1977. Having been assigned to the cardiac catheterization*
service at the University of Florida, I was making afternoon rounds,
seeing patients who were to be catheterized the next day. The second
patient on the schedule was a 52-year-old night watchman from a rural
town in northern Florida. The intern's admission note on his chart indicated that the patient had suffered a massive heart attack in December
1973 and had continued to have progressively severe chest pain despite
increasing medical therapy. The records sent by his local physician noted
that the patient had suffered a cardiac arrest at the time of his heart
attack in 1973.

After giving him a routine briefing on his forthcoming catheterization, I asked him to reconstruct the events of his 1973 heart attack. He
remembered the day quite well. He had been under treatment for several
months by his local physician for chest pains which had been attributed
to hiatal hernia, an abnormality of the stomach. That day, chest pain
had begun following a large noon meal. He took his prescribed medications but the pain worsened. That evening, it became so unbearable that

* Cardiac catheterization is a specialized X-ray technique performed by cardiologists to
reveal the presence and extent of damage to the heart and major blood vessels.

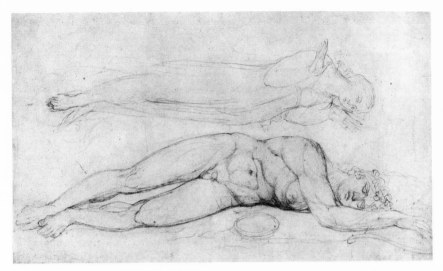

The Soul Hovering Over the Body Reluctantly Parting with Life by William Blake, 1805. The Tate Gallery, London.
   A nineteenth-century conception of the moment of death. The "soul" is seen departing from the physical body and looking down from above, as does the "separated self" in modern-day descriptions of autoscopic NDE.

he drove to the nearest town that had a community hospital. He checked into the emergency room and was evaluated by the ER physician. After some delay, he was told that he was having a bad attack from his hernia, was given some shots and told to return home. As he was walking down the emergency room hall he suddenly "blacked out." The next thing he recalled was lying face up on a stretcher on his way to the intensive care unit.

Asked to recollect anything that happened after he apparently blacked out, he reached for a cigarette and lit up slowly. He glanced over at the door to make sure no one else was listening. Then came the by-now-familiar "Why do you want to know?" I gave him the standard response. Cautiously he began describing his experience.

The session that followed entailed some fifteen to twenty cigarettes and two hours of tape. His near-death experience is presented, in part, below:

> I couldn't stand the pain any more. . . . And then I collapsed. That's when everything went dark. . . . After a little while . . . I was sitting up there somewhere and I could look down, and I had never noticed that the floor was black and white tile. That's the first thing I re-

member being conscious of. . . . I recognized myself down there, sort of curled around in a half-fetal position. Two or three people lifted me and put me up on a tray, not a tray but a dolly. . . . They strapped my legs and started moving me. When they first threw me up on the table [the doctor] struck me, and I mean he really whacked the hell out of me. He came back with his fist from way behind his head and he hit me right in the center of my chest. And then they were pushing on my chest. . . . They shoved a plastic tube, like you put in an oil can, they shoved that in my mouth. . . . It was at that point I noticed another table-like arrangement with a bunch of stuff on it. I knew it later to be the machine that they thump you with. . . . I could see my right ear and this side of my face because I was facing away. . . . I could hear people talking. . . . It [the cardiac monitor] was like an oscilloscope. It made the same streak, over and over. . . . They put a needle in me—like one of those Aztec Indian rituals where they take the virgin's heart out. They took it two-handed—I thought this very unusual. . . . [Then they took these] round disks with a handle on them. . . . They put one up here—I think it was larger than the other one—and they put one down here [patient pointed to appropriate positions on chest]. . . . They thumped me and I didn't respond. . . . I thought they had given my body too much voltage. Man, my body jumped about two feet off the table. . . . It appeared to me in some sort of fashion that I had a choice to reenter my body and take the chance of them bringing me back around or I could just go ahead and die, if I wasn't already dead. . . . I knew I was going to be perfectly safe, whether my body died or not. . . . They thumped me a second time. . . . I reentered my body just like that. (I-19)

At the end of this exhausting but fascinating interview, I thanked him for his willingness to discuss his experience and reassured him about his catheterization the next morning. As he seemed eager, I promised him that we would meet again to talk of his experience and discuss any further thoughts that he might have about it. (I subsequently followed this patient until my departure from Florida in July 1978. We had many long conversations about this experience and a related experience he encountered during his open-heart operation in January 1978; see page 64).

Before leaving the hospital that night, I carefully reviewed the medical details of his cardiac arrest to supplement his description of the resuscitation. His records sent by a local physician documented that a 49-year-old Caucasian male had signed into the emergency room of the community hospital at 7:43 P.M. on that night in December. He was complaining of severe chest pain of several hours' duration. After being checked by the ER physician, he was given 50 mg of Demerol (a narcotic pain killer) intramuscularly and advised to return home. Tentative diagnosis—hiatal hernia. At 9:35 P.M., he was found without pulse or respiration on the emergency room floor. Cardiopulmonary resuscitation including external cardiac massage was immediately begun. Intravenous and/or intracardiac medications were administered, though the route of administration was not specified. Two 400 watt-second cardioversions (electric shocks to the chest to stabilize cardiac rhythm) were given at 9:37 and 9:39 P.M., after which the man regained consciousness and was transported to the intensive care unit. Final admitting diagnosis—acute myocardial infarction (heart attack) with cardiac arrest.

This man described his NDE as if he had separated from his physical self and "visually" observed objects and events in the vicinity of his unconscious body. Such an experience was recalled by thirty-two persons in this study. Previous authors have identified this portion of the NDE as an "out-of-body" experience. Indeed, these descriptions of bodily separation and visualization of the physical self and its surroundings from a detached, elevated position fit well with the concept of an out-of-(physical)-body experience. However, as we shall see, additional portions of the NDE (i.e., the transcendental elements) are also described by the near-death survivor as if they had occurred "out of body." Thus the term "out of body" could apply to *all* portions of the NDE. Since my analysis of the NDE in later chapters considers the self-visualizing aspects of the experience separately from other (transcendental) elements, I have chosen to distinguish the portion of the NDE described in this chapter by calling it the *autoscopic* (self-visualizing) *NDE*.

During the autoscopic experience, the "self" which had "separated" from the unconscious physical body was perceived to be situated above the level of the physical body—a point specifically identified as "ceiling height" in all but three cases. These three exceptions included a 69-year-old man who stated that he "could look down and directly see my body and face lying in bed about 150 feet below" (I–27); an army colonel who described his NDE, during a cardiac arrest in December 1975, as if he were "flying . . . high over Womack so [that] I was looking down into the room [intensive care unit] where they had taken my body" (I–42); and a

60-year-old man from Michigan who claimed that during his cardiac arrest in 1976, "I was looking from up, down. I was, say, about sixty feet up. I was going up slowly, like floating in a dark or semidark corridor like. They were working the hell out of me [his physical body]." (I–57)

"Visualized" Details

These "visual" perceptions were described as being clear and distinct in all but three cases. Even when the person felt that his "visual" perception of ongoing events was not distinct, considerable detail of the resuscitation could still be recalled. To wit: a 66-year-old mail clerk was admitted to the University of Florida emergency room in December 1977, with a massive heart attack. While undergoing evaluation in the emergency room, he suffered a prolonged cardiac arrest, which required eight separate electrical shocks (cardioversions) to the chest before cardiac rhythm was restored. When interviewed shortly thereafter, he told me that after he had "blacked out," he found himself "standing in the doorway" of the emergency room, watching his resuscitation. Although he "saw things somewhat fuzzy," he was able to discern "visually" the initial chest thump ("they beat the shit out of my chest"), the shape and color of the defibrillator paddles used to "shock" his heart, and the general appearance of his physical body during the artifical respiration and electrical shocks. (I–13).

Of the autoscopic visualizations that were "clear and distinct," many were reported in considerable detail. The following experience was described by a 44-year-old man who had suffered a massive heart attack and cardiac arrest in the intensive care unit during his second hospital day. His resuscitation required multiple electric shocks to the chest. From his vantage point detached from his physical body, he was able to observe carefully and then later to recall, among other things, the movement of the meter needles on the face of the machine (defibrillator) that delivered the electric shock to his chest. He had never seen a defibrillator in use before.

> It was almost like I was detached, standing off to the side and watching it all going on, not being a participant at all but being an uninterested observer.... The first thing they did was to put an injection into the IV, the rubber gasket they have there for pushes. ... Then they lifted me up and moved me onto the plywood. That's

when Dr. A began to do the pounding on the chest. . . . They had oxygen on me before, one of those little nose tubes, and they took that off and put on a face mask which covers your mouth and nose. It was a type of pressure thing . . . sort of a soft plastic mask, light green color. . . . I remember them pulling over the cart, the defibrillator, the thing with the paddles on it. . . . It had a meter on the face. . . . It was square and had two needles on there, one fixed and one which moved. . . . [The needle] seemed to come up rather slowly, really. It didn't just pop up like an ammeter or a voltmeter or something registering. . . . The first time it went between ⅓ and ½ scale. And then they did it again, and this time it went up over ½ scale, and the third time it was about ¾. . . . The fixed needle moved each time they punched the thing and somebody was messing with it. And I think they moved the fixed needle and it stayed still while the other one moved up. . . . [The defibrillator] had a bunch of dials on it. It was on wheels with a little railing around the thing, and they had stuff on it. And they had the two paddle affairs with wires attached . . . like a round disk with handles on them. . . . They held one in each hand and they put it across my chest. . . . I think it was like a handle with little buttons on it. . . . I could see myself jolt. (I–32)

Another "visual" description of a near-death crisis event—this time a grand mal seizure associated with severe toxemia of pregnancy seventeen years previously—was given by a 37-year-old housewife as if she had been seated in a "balcony looking down." According to her, this was the only seizure she had ever witnessed.

I knew something was going to happen . . . and then I went unconscious . . . and I was looking down and could see myself going into convulsions, and I was starting to fall out of bed, and the girl in the next bed screaming for the nurses. . . . The nurse caught me and put me back and by then there were two other nurses there and one came back almost immediately with a tongue depressor on my tongue. And they got the sides up on the bed and they called the doctor. . . . It was a feeling of height, great distance, a light feeling, *like being up in a balcony* looking down and watching all this and feeling very detached as though I was watching someone else, like you might watch a movie. . . . It was a very calm, relaxed feeling, a feeling of well-being if anything. . . . Everything was clearly seen, like watching television. . . . It looked very ugly to me to see my body thrashing around on the bed . . . and the way I was jerking around . . . was very frightening to the girl in the other bed. . . . The convulsion didn't last very long and the next thing I was aware of, I don't know how the change takes place, but I woke up the next morning and I was back to me again. (I–28–2)

A 60-year-old Ohio housewife suffered a cardiac arrest while hospitalized in January 1978. During the episode, according to this woman:

I had left my body and was to the side in sort of like a tube. . . . They called the express team and I could see them coming in and all the doctors and nurses and all the confusion. . . . They were punching my chest, putting IVs in me; they were all rushing around. . . . Some of the others were packing my belongings because they were going to take me up to ICU [the intensive care unit] . . . I could see their faces and the backs of the ones who had their backs to me. . . . I could see the little needle they were putting in my hand. Something about the blood gases. . . . I could see my face very clearly, and they were lifting my eyelids. They were pulling my eyelids up to look to see where my eyes were, I guess. That's the only way I can explain it. Then they were feeling around my neck where the pulse is. Most of the time it was just this pushing on my chest. . . . They had the breathing machine and a cart with a whole bunch of stuff on it, but I don't know what all those things were. . . . I had seen them grabbing all this stuff out of my locker, which was right at the foot of my bed. I could see around the backs of these people, and I saw this one girl grabbing everything because the doctor had said, "We're going to have to get her up to ICU." She was grabbing everything out of my drawer and dumping it into bags and suitcases. When I came to, everything was labeled with my name on it, to go upstairs. . . . But the breathing thing they put on my face. It was just a cone-shaped thing that went over my nose. When the doctor was pushing on my chest, they had this on me. . . .

A: Could you see behind your head?
S: No. I didn't even think about looking back there because all the action was right in front of me. (I–45–2)

A 50-year-old real estate broker described the events of his cardiac arrest and NDE, which occurred in the intensive care unit of a Florida hospital in January 1975:

Then I got my chest pain and passed out. I don't remember anything for a while, and the next thing I remember I was hanging on the ceiling looking down on them working on my body. . . . She [the nurse] put a needle in there and was shooting it into the IV. . . . Everything was there just like it always was there—the nightstand, the chair, everything I could think of. . . . It looked like he [the doctor] had one hand on my chest and he kept hitting it real hard. I could see the bed moving up and down . . . It [the cardiac monitor] wasn't running at that time. The red light was on and there was a line across. Instead of running up and down like, there was just a line across. It seems that whatever they had done got the monitor running again. That's when I got back in bed. (I–14)

These people who had observed their own physical bodies from this "out-of-body" state would describe a total absence of pain even while they underwent painful medical procedures without anesthesia. One 44-year-old Florida resident made the following remarks about his resuscitation from a cardiac arrest, which he had observed in a painless, detached state: "That's when Dr. A began to do the pounding on the chest, and it didn't hurt even though it cracked a rib. I felt no pain. . . . [During defibrillation] I could see myself jolt, but again, it didn't hurt like an electric shock should hurt." (I–32)

The Ohio woman mentioned above likewise noted her lack of pain as she watched the resuscitation of her physical body in 1978:

I can remember I couldn't feel them when they were probing to put the needle in. That was unusual because you can usually feel that. I also didn't feel anything when they were pushing on my chest. All I saw was them doing it, but I didn't feel a thing. . . . This is the first time I can honestly say an IV didn't hurt me. (I–45–2)

Hearing

In addition to the "visual" observation of ongoing events, sixteen persons stated that they could hear the conversation in the vicinity of their physical body during an autoscopic NDE. A 62-year-old man who experienced a cardiac arrest and autoscopic NDE claimed: "I could hear them and see them working on me and hear them talking and giving them orders and directions. It seemed like I was above my body." (I–67) Another cardiac-arrest patient reported similarly: "I remember I was hanging on the ceiling looking down at them working on my body. . . . I heard the doctor talking to my nurse. I think I can remember him telling her what to get and things like that. Yes, I heard that." (I–14)

A 57-year-old construction worker was unable to hear during his cardiac arrest and autoscopic NDE, but could do so as his NDE ended:

> I was sort of in a floating position. . . . I recognized me laying there. And they were moving me back and forth in the bed but I couldn't see what else they were doing 'cause there were so many of them bent over me. . . . I couldn't hear anything. Some of these articles you read, the people say they can hear everything. I couldn't hear anything. . . . I did go on back in [my body] and that was it. . . . Then one of them said, "He doesn't have any blood pressure yet," and another replied, "As soon as this atropine hits his heart he will." Then I felt flushed and then they started talking to me. (I–5)

Another survivor of a cardiac arrest stated that during his autoscopic NDE, "I couldn't hear but I could see everything there." (I–63–2)

Attempted Communication with Others

Five persons attempted to communicate with others physically present at the time of their autoscopic experience. From her "out-of-body" state, a 37-year-old woman desired to contact her mother, who was present at the time of her NDE, but "I couldn't somehow let her know that I was all right. Somehow I knew I was all right, but I didn't know how to tell her. I just watched." (I–28–1) A 51-year-old man also attempted to tell others he was "O.K." during his autoscopic NDE: "I was able to see that I was not there. I had left. I said, 'If anybody can hear me, I am going to be O.K.'" (I–3) Direct communication with a nurse was attempted by the construction worker cited above:

> I seen my [physical] face. It was about four feet below me and I could see it. . . . I could see they [doctors and nurses] were busy. In fact, one time a nurse I could see looked me right in the [nonphysical] face just this far away [indicating one foot]. I tried to say something, but she didn't say nothing. . . . She was like looking at a movie screen that can't talk back and that doesn't recognize you're there. I was the real one and she was unreal. That's the way I felt." (I–5)

Perhaps the most dramatic example of attempted communication between the near-death victim in the "out-of-body" state and others physically present at the time was described by a 33-year-old Vietnam veteran who lost both legs and an arm following a mine explosion. His autoscopic NDE began on the battlefield at the time of the explosion and continued as his unconscious body was transported by helicopter to the nearest field hospital. He remained with his body all this time. While in the operating room in the field hospital, "watching" his own operation, he tried to stop the surgeon from saving his life:

> S: I'm trying to stop them [the doctors]. I really did try to grab a hold of them and stop them, because I really felt happy where I was. . . . I actually remember grabbing the doctor. . . .
>
> A: What happened?
>
> S: Nothing. Absolutely nothing. It was almost like he wasn't there. I grabbed and he wasn't there or either I just went through him or whatever. (I–68)

"Thought Travel"

Three persons described the ability to move voluntarily while suspended above their body in this "out-of-body" state. This movement was seemingly accomplished through the equivalent of "thought travel."

The Vietnam veteran alluded to above felt at one point as if he had "left" the operating room where his physical body lay and had "traveled" back to the battlefield, where other American soldiers were picking up the dead:

> While they are doing this [surgery], I remember all of a sudden going right back to the battlefield where I had been lost. They were cleaning up after the battle. I am watching all these men that had died that day and they were putting them in those ponchos and picking up the wounded. One of the group I knew, and I remember distinctly trying to get him to stop from picking up those bodies. I couldn't do it and all of a sudden I was right back in the medevac place. . . . It was almost like you materialize there and all of a sudden the next instant you were over here. It was just like you blinked your eyes.

Such "travel" was also described by the night watchman whose cardiac arrest and autoscopic NDE were reported at the beginning of this chapter. While "out of body," he had the following sensation: "Are you familiar with a telephoto lens? I could adjust that at will. I could bring the subject closer to me or me closer to the subject. I could just think:

Hey, it would be nice to be a little closer to the subject—I would just be there." This "travel" purportedly carried him to nearby locations which were outside the emergency room in which his resuscitation was taking place.

> I could see anywhere I wanted to. I could see out in the parking lot, but I was still in the corridor. . . . It was just like I said, "O.K., what's going on out in the parking lot?" and part of my brain would go over and take a look at what's going on over there and come back and report to me, or I don't know. . . . I thought they were making a hell of a racket in the place where they did the laundry. They had big boilers in there and I thought: Gee, that's too much racket. I'm sure the patients above on the next floor have got to hear that. Why don't they pad those doors? Why don't they put acoustical tile up? . . . I did have an occasion to go in the cafeteria when I was back there visiting someone [months later], and it was just like the way it was when I visualized it. The same details—but this is something I was not going to tell you. (I–19)

Another man described a similar ability to "travel" while "out of body" during an autoscopic NDE and cardiac arrest in February 1976:

> I could have moved away from my body anytime I wanted to. . . . There wasn't a thing that was mechanical about it, like an automobile or anything. It was just a thought process. I felt like I could have thought myself anywhere I wanted to be instantly. . . . I just felt exhilarated with a sense of power. I could do what I wanted to. . . . It's realer than here, really. (I–65)

The Return

All the people interviewed remarked that during the autoscopic NDE, they felt as if they had been truly "separated" from their physical body. Likewise, at the end of the experience, a "return" to the physical body was felt to have taken place, in order, as one woman put it, to "become whole again." Following this "return," the person either regained consciousness in the physical body or lapsed back into an unconscious state, to awaken physically at some later point.

This "return" from an autoscopic NDE was often described as an instantaneous event which coincided with a particular resuscitative measure, observed immediately prior to the end of the experience. An electric

shock to the chest was identified as the terminating event of an autoscopic NDE encountered by a 62-year-old aircraft mechanic during a
cardiac arrest in March 1978:

> I was above myself, looking down. They was working on me, trying
> to bring me back. . . . I seen them trying to bring me back with
> those pads [the defibrillator]. They put something on those pads like
> a lubricant, it looked like, and rubbed them together and put them
> on my body. And then it jumped. But I couldn't feel it, even at that
> time. They brought it back and then hit it again. . . . At that time I
> thought about my family and all and I said, "Maisie, I better go
> back." It was just as if I went back and got into my body. . . . That's
> when they brought me back and that's when I come back to my
> body. (I–67)

Two other survivors of cardiac arrests claimed to have had their
autoscopic NDEs abruptly end with cardiac defibrillation:

> The nurse was on this side of the bed with that machine. She picked
> up them shocker things and put one there and one right there
> [pointing to appropriate places on chest] and I seen my body flop
> like that. . . . It seemed like it just took me and slammed me right
> together, you know. It seemed like I was apart and then like two
> forces coming together in a crash. It seemed like I was up here
> [pointing to ceiling] and it grabbed me and my body and forced it
> back, pushed it back. (I–63–2)

> I was sitting up there somewhere and I could look down. . . . They
> thumped me a second time. . . . Then I reentered my body—a tran-
> sition that was just like that [the snap of a finger]. (I–19)

An autoscopic NDE during a postoperative coma not associated
with a cardiac arrest apparently ended when someone arrived at the
door of the woman patient's hospital room: ". . . and suddenly I was up
at the ceiling . . . and looked right down on the bed and saw my body.
Then when someone in the family came to the door and called . . . I was
instantaneously back in my body." (I–46)

Occasionally, the "return" from the autoscopic NDE was spontaneous, unrelated to any event "witnessed" by the unconscious person while
in the "out-of-body" state. For instance, a 38-year-old Florida farmer
felt as if he had "reentered" his body during a brief cardiac arrest in a
parking lot: "I was looking down on my own body . . . then the next

thing . . . I was back in my body." (I–20) Presumably, this man's experience ended with the spontaneous resumption of his heartbeat—an event that occurred several times during his subsequent hospitalization.

A 60-year-old woman hospitalized in January 1978 had the experience of watching her resuscitation from an "out-of-body" location and then of suddenly feeling that she "was back there in all the action" in her physical body. (I–45–2) She could not relate her physical "reentrance" to any one resuscitative measure she had witnessed at the time, however.

Telling Others

Several persons who had encountered an autoscopic NDE said they had later mentioned these experiences to others who were present while it ensued. In each case, these witnesses were quite surprised at the accuracy of the patient's observations. One woman described the reaction of her mother and her physician on hearing some of the details of her autoscopic experience:

> Then I started telling her [mother] that I had known that I was going to die, but she didn't understand how I knew this. . . . Mother was shocked that I knew what the doctor had said when he had checked me and about her crying and sitting with me all night and praying. . . . She knew that I knew what had gone on in the room. . . . I remember them [mother and doctor] discussing that they didn't understand how I knew or how I could know that I was unconscious. It was just dropped at that. (I–28–1)

Following his cardiac resuscitation, a man described the procedure to his physician:

> And when I mentioned a couple of things that he [the doctor] had done, really, that's what made him think, "Well, I did do that. I know you were unconscious, so you must have seen." There were a few things, and I don't remember them now, that he felt like I just had to have seen or would not have known that he had done them. (I–14)

The physician of another survivor of a cardiac arrest was confronted with the details of the resuscitation by his patient the following day in the intensive care unit of a Florida hospital:

When Dr. B seen me, he told me I had a close call and died and all that stuff. I told him, "Dr. B, I couldn't have died. I knew everything that went on." I told him when he came up under my right armpit and changed his mind and went to the other side. He said it was impossible and that I couldn't have possibly seen that and that I was legally dead at that time. He just shook his head. He just couldn't understand it. And I asked, "Am I right?" He said, "Yes, you're right!" He just shook his head and went walking off. (I–67)

To verify these autoscopic "visualizations," however, the details of the experiences must be independently documented either from firsthand accounts of others present at the time (doctors, nurses, etc.) or from descriptions of the resuscitative events in medical records. Such documentation was available in many instances and will be presented in Chapter 7. But first we must look at what appears to be a deeper realm of the NDE—the transcendental experience.

Ascension to the Empyrean by Hieronymus Bosch. Palace of the Doges, Venice. Scala/Editorial Photocolor Archives.

This sixteenth-century painting depicts death as a journey through darkness and a tunnel into a brilliant light and beyond, a conception that bears a striking resemblance to modern-day descriptions of the transcendental NDE.

4

The Transcendental Near-Death Experience

JULY 1978: I had recently begun my assignment as staff cardiologist at the Atlanta VA Medical Center. The last patient I was scheduled to see one day entered my office about 4 P.M. I was immediately struck by the discrepancy between his youthful, healthy appearance and the thick medical record that lay before me. He seemingly defied a basic medical rule: the thicker the chart, the sicker the patient.

A quick glance at his medical records told the story. Despite his thirty-five years, he had suffered a massive heart attack in May 1977. Since that time, he had been in and out of the hospital, with chest pain and heart failure. In spite of these physical setbacks, he apparently had been able to maintain a cheerful, optimistic outlook on life.

Introducing myself as his new cardiologist, I reviewed his medical regimen with him. His condition was quite stable at that moment, so I renewed his prescriptions and scheduled another appointment. As he was preparing to leave I happened to notice Problem No. 15 on the medical problem list at the front of all Emory University charts. It read: "Cardiac arrest from an acute inferior myocardial infarction." I sat him back down.

The circumstances for an interview couldn't have been more favorable. He was the last patient I was scheduled to see that day, and he was in no particular hurry. His story unfolded as follows.

In May 1977, he and his wife were out dancing with friends. While dancing, he began experiencing severe chest pain. Thinking it was indigestion, he went outside to get some fresh air, but the pain persisted. One of his friends convinced him to go to the local emergency room, where he was given a hurried examination. Then he blacked out, awakening the next day attached to a cardiac monitor, with intravenous solutions running into his arm. During this period, he had the following experience:

> I remember reaching the hospital entrance and them dragging me out of the car. That's when I started going out. . . . I remember them saying, "He's had a heart attack." I went out then. . . . During this stage, my life just flashed in front of my face. My whole life . . . Things that had happened to me in my lifetime, like when we got married, just flashed in front of my eyes, flashed and it was gone. When we . . . had our first child flashed in front of my eyes. The biggest thing, I guess, and the longest thing that stayed flashing in front of my eyes, was when I accepted Jesus Christ, and that was a few years ago. That's when I went into a tunnel. I just felt like I was in a rolling tunnel, black tunnel. Just darkness. At the end of that tunnel was a glowing light. It looked like an orange—uh—you seen the sunset in the afternoon? From the light it makes up an orange glow with a yellow tint in a circle. That's what it looked like at the end of that tunnel. . . . I was just in a peaceful state of mind. It was the most experienced thing I ever had and I just didn't care whether I woke up or not. It was relaxed. The whole thing was just relaxed after that. . . . I remember hearing voices . . . I think it was Jesus Christ who was talking to me. . . . I seen the—uh—golden gates of heaven, I guess. I seen the steps. I remember seeing those. . . . I was walking up some steps that I shouldn't have been walking up and I don't know how I got there but I was there. . . . Some words were spoken to me by somebody and I was right back to sleep again. (I–15)

Quoting from his hospital discharge summary:

> This 35-year-old Caucasian male developed the onset of dull substernal chest pain while dancing. He was brought to the ER and admitted to intensive care unit. In the ER, it was felt he had an

acute inferior myocardial infarction [heart attack] by electrocardiogram and had a sinus bradycardia [slow heart rate]. Upon being
received in the ICU, he went into ventricular fibrillation [cardiac
arrest] and was defibrillated [electric shock to chest]. He went into
ventricular fibrillation about 10–11 times and was defibrillated.
Eventually this ended. . . .

He remained in intensive care until May 27, 1977, and then was
moved to the general medical ward. He recovered and was discharged, to
be followed by his local physician. He was later referred to the Atlanta
VA Medical Center for cardiac catheterization and follow-up care,
which is still continuing.

This man had vividly perceived the passage of his "consciousness"
into a foreign region or dimension quite apart from the "earthly" surroundings of his physical body. I have labeled such an experience the
transcendental NDE, since it contains descriptions of objects and events
that "transcend" or surpass our earthly limits. In all, forty-one such
descriptions were reported by people in this study.

The Dark Region or Void

For fourteen persons, the transcendental experience began with the feeling of entering a dark region or void. Momentary fright or bewilderment
sometimes accompanied the initial passage into darkness, as the person
pondered: What is going on here? In time, however, these unpleasant
emotions were replaced with calm, peace or tranquility, as further elements of the NDE began to unfold. Some people felt as if they were
suspended motionless within this dark void. Such was the case with a
47-year-old Florida electrician, who, following resuscitation from a cardiac arrest in March 1977, described it this way: "I just entered a total
dark soundless void. Seems like you're just laying out there in darkness."
(I–33) Other persons perceived a definite sense of movement through
this region of darkness. During an episode of postoperative shock, a 23-
year-old woman felt this way:

> There was total blackness around me. I want to say that it felt like I
> was moving very, very fast in time and space. I was traveling
> through a tunnel. It didn't look like a tunnel, but when you're in a
> tunnel, all you see is blackness around you. If you move very fast
> you can feel the sides moving in on you whether there are sides
> there or not because of the darkness. (I–29)

Another man was resuscitated from three separate cardiac arrests within an hour of admission to a north Florida hospital in April 1977. He was quickly cardioverted during the first two arrests and described a motionless "suspension" within a dark void on both occasions. The third arrest was more prolonged and was associated with a sense of "movement" through this dark void:

[Arrest 1.] Everything was black. Then a floating sensation, like spacelessness like they have in a space program. I wasn't floating in any direction, but it was like I was hanging there.

[Arrest 2.] Then I had the same feeling of floating, not upward or any direction, but just floating.

[Arrest 3.] I remember the black enfolding me again. . . . This time, instead of having the sensation of just hanging in space, I had the sensation of going up. Like I was lifting up. I had the sensation of going up. (I–56)

In two cases, this region of darkness was perceived while the person was still in the autoscopic portion of the NDE. One such case involved a sixty-year-old woman who "watched" her cardiac resuscitation, in January 1978, from an "out-of-body" location while surrounded by a region of darkness:

[During the arrest] I had left my body and was to the side in sort of like a tube. It was real dark in there, but I could see what they were doing. I could hear them. I saw them doing all this stuff to me. . . . Just like you would put a big tube off to the side of the bed, and I just slid from the bed right into that tube, just drifted in there. . . . But around my body it was light, just like a room would be. Whatever I was in was black, but I could see out and watch everything. (I–45–2)

In the other case, a man felt he was moving through a dark, corridor-like region while observing the resuscitation of his unconscious physical body:

I could see my body lying there. . . . I saw the whole show. . . . I was going up slowly, like floating in a dark or semidark corridor like. They were working the hell out of me. . . . And I kept thinking: What is this? What's happening? And I kept going up and up and up. . . . And then I went further. . . . I went to a different world. (I–57)

In this last case, the dark, corridor-like region separated the autoscopic perceptions of earthly events from the other-world features of a transcendental experience.

Light

Seventeen persons described a brilliant source of light which signaled the end of the dark region or void and the beginning of a transcendental environment of great beauty. "Movement" was toward this light and away from the region of darkness. A 56-year-old executive from Florida described it this way:

> I went through this period of darkness.... There was this light, like someone holding a flashlight, and I started going towards that. And then the whole thing brightened up and the next thing I remember was I was floating.... We were going through this shaft of light ... the light kept getting brighter and brighter.... It was so bright, and the closer we got, the brighter it got, and it was blinding.
>
> A: Was it irritating?
> S: No. There was no part of the experience that was irritating. (I–8)

This light was often compared to the brightness of the sun or the beauty of a sunset.

A 35-year-old survivor of a cardiac arrest:

> At the end of that tunnel was a glowing light. It looked like an orange—uh—you seen the sunset in the afternoon? From the light it makes up an orange glow with a yellow tint in a circle. That's what it looked like at the end of that tunnel. I never did reach the end of that tunnel. (I–15)

A 45-year-old pharmaceutical salesman during a cardiac arrest:

> I went out the window. I guess you've flown an airplane into the clouds when the sun shone on it? All it was was a bright light that got brighter and brighter but it didn't hurt your eyes. (I–60)

A 33-year-old soldier during a mine explosion in Vietnam in 1969:

> ... a very bright, bright light. It wasn't the sun and yet it was like

an overexposed picture of you shooting the camera into the sun. All you've got is the white background and all you see is the white around you. (I-68)

A 54-year-old ex-mechanic who had recovered from an episode of profound shock in 1972 pictured this light to be "the absence of darkness."

My description of the light was—well, it was not a light but the absence of darkness, total and complete. . . . Well, you think of light as a big light shining on things making shadows and so forth. This light was really the absence of darkness. We're not used to that concept because we always get a shadow from a light unless the light is all around us. But this light was so total and complete that you didn't look at the light, you were *in* the light. See what I'm saying? (I-65)

Yet another description of the light was given by a 51-year-old man resuscitated from a cardiac arrest in August 1972:

Then I saw light, but a bright light, I mean such a bright light, and it had the shape of—if you watch TV, there's an advertisement for Quasar television that has these little white lights that just brighten up and are not exactly in the form of a cross but are basically a cross except they have a little more flare in the center part. That is approximately what I saw in extreme intensity, brightness. (I-3)

In two cases, the light was interpreted as being the spirit of a person or a religious figure. For example, a 53-year-old survivor of a cardiac arrest in 1977 felt it to be "two people":

There was a big white light, but it wasn't like one man but maybe it was two in light. It wasn't a blinding, bright light at all. It was just a white light which looked like two people, but other than that, I actually didn't see who it was . . . like two people that were coming toward me. Although I couldn't distinguish them as people. Just outlines of light. (I-56)

The Transcendental Environment

A region of scenic beauty was perceived by twenty-eight persons during their transcendental NDE. Descriptions of this transcendental environment varied considerably (see Table XII). However, this "place" was never recognized as a previously visited location (i.e., it was not a déjà vu phenomenon). The "visit" was felt to be a vivid out-of-body excursion—as if a brief sojourn had actually been taken to a physical location.

Scenes of pastoral, earthly beauty were portrayed by eleven persons. A 55-year-old textile mill laborer told of the following landscape, encountered during a cardiac arrest in January 1979:

> During this vision that I had, I couldn't see myself but I was standing on something high because down below me there was just the most beautiful, greenest pasture. There was just a small hill and then just flat meadow over to my right. . . . I was looking down on these cattle and sheep and on this shepherd, and they were in a meadow like, with cattle on the right and sheep on the left, and he was standing on just like a round knoll twenty or thirty feet high. . . . It was just like a bright sunshiny day. . . . The whole outline of it looked like a putting green on a well-kept golf course. . . . He had his back to me, but it was just like you see in the Bible. He had on this long robe and a cloth over his head with a band around it, and he was there holding something. I saw a staff, but I don't know. . . . I don't know specifically who it was. . . . Oh, I can see it now. It is just so stamped in my mind that it will never go away, I don't believe. (I–66)

A 63-year-old man who had spent much of his life in Texas felt that during his cardiac arrest in 1969 he hovered over a barbed-wire fence which separated two entirely different scenes:

> I was suspended over a fence. . . . On one side of the fence it was extremely scraggly territory, mesquite brush and generally a junky place you wouldn't want to be. On the other side of the fence was the most beautiful pasture scene I guess I have ever seen in my life or even imagined, within the distance some beautiful trees, beautiful grass, and horses. . . . [It was] a three- or four-strand barbed-wire fence. . . . The fence was a definite dividing line, with the beautiful green grass coming right up to the fence and stopping. . . . The left was the world, here, the world. The scraggly dirty place is where I live. . . . The other place is where I am going. (I–47)

A stream of water was the dominant feature of a 32-year-old Florida housewife's experience during a deep coma from liver and kidney failure:

It's just like a still stream of water. You can walk across. And there's rainbow colors in the background and it looks like a rainbow. (I–18)

Another Florida housewife, during a cardiac arrest in 1977:

It was like a beautiful sunglow and sunset. It wasn't any blue sky or green water. The water he [her deceased husband] was coming to me in was in a yellow glow. . . . And everything was just beautiful. The trees were there but they were all in the shadows of gold. There was no green, no blue. (I–34)

"Nonterrestrial" scenes of clouds, skies, stars or a mist were recalled by eight persons. During a cardiac arrest, a 69-year-old Florida man felt as if he were "walking on clouds [on a] clear, beautiful summer day with clear sky." (I–27) Another man, in the midst of a postoperative cardiac arrest, viewed deceased relatives "standing in clouds. They were kind of bright, but there was a dark cloud behind them. . . . I was floating through the clouds." (I–44) A 55-year-old public health nurse encountered her deceased father sitting "outdoors" in a "mist" during a postoperative coma. (I–37) And a 60-year-old man related that during his NDE, "the world split . . . everything was silver . . . like diamonds and stars." (I–25)

Ethereal, heavenly descriptions were given by nine persons, and commonly included a gate perceived to be the entrance to heaven. During a cardiac arrest and NDE, a 35-year-old Georgia businessman found himself "walking up some steps that I shouldn't have been walking up . . . [which led to] the golden gates of heaven." (I–15) The gates of heaven, with "people on the other side of the gate" (I–43), were depicted by one Florida woman following her cardiac arrest. Another man described a "gold ornamental gate, wrought-iron in appearance, with a highly polished color." (I–61)

In two cases, these ethereal scenes were simply "beyond words": "It was just beautiful up there . . . ethereal beauty. . . . What anybody would imagine heaven to be. The beauty of things was ethereal. It was altogether ethereal" (I–54); and "a beautiful panorama . . . just beyond words." (I–65)

Encountering Others

The nearness of some other personage was perceived by twenty-eight persons during their NDE. This personage was recognized as either a nonvisual "presence" or a visualized "spirit." Communication between the near-death person and this spiritual being could be recalled in twenty-one cases. The *method* of communication varied: "verbal" in twelve cases (e.g., "clear, loud voice"; "loud, thundering voice"; "words"); nonverbal "telepathy" in four cases (e.g., "without talking with our voices"; "it just registered in my brain"); nonverbal gestures in two cases (e.g., "outstretched arms"; "waving of the hand"); and a combination of the verbal and the nonverbal in three cases. The *content* of this communication most frequently focused on a decision to either proceed further into the experience (i.e., "to die") or "return" to the physical body and live (see Table XIII).

The presence of God or Jesus was identified by three persons, including a 51-year-old Protestant salesman who suffered a cardiac arrest in 1972:

> I remember asking or speaking out in a clear, loud voice, at least what I thought was loud: "Jesus Christ, please give me more time with my children." And I don't think at any time in my life I ever, ever felt more humble or more sincere about anything than at that time when I asked. It was almost as if—and I'm not trying to dramatize and I hope it doesn't sound that way—I almost knew I was talking to God. I was that close. . . . I felt the sincerity and did ask Jesus Christ for more time with my children. (I–3)

Two persons described the presence of deceased friends or relatives during their NDE. Such was the case with a seriously wounded soldier as he lay unconscious on the battlefield viewing his own body:

> I came out of my body, and I perceived me laying on the ground with three limbs gone. . . . What makes this so real was that the thirteen guys that had been killed the day before that I had put in plastic bags were right there with me. And more than that, during the course of that month of May, my particular company lost forty-two dead. All forty-two of those guys were there. They were not in the form we perceive the human body, and I can't tell you what form they were in because I don't know. But I know they were there. I felt their presence. We communicated without talking with our voices. . . . There was no sympathy, no sorrow. They were already where they were. They didn't want to go back. That was the basic tone of our communication . . . that we were all happy right where we were. (I–68)

A 52-year-old Florida man felt the presence of his deceased brother while "suspended" over his unconscious physical body during a cardiac arrest in 1973:

> I was sitting up there somewhere and I could look down. . . . [With me was] my older brother, who had been dead since I was a young fella. I couldn't see, but I knew he was right by me, even patting me on the shoulder, saying, "It's entirely up to you—you can do anything you want to do. If you want to stay and you don't want to go back, in your body, and you see how bad shape it's in, you can stay and I'll be right by your side and everything is going to be fine." (I–19)

The presence could not definitely be identified in four instances. A 54-year-old ex-mechanic, following an episode of unconsciousness and shock in 1972, put it this way:

> I was with an angel or God or somebody that I had total harmony with but with total communication without saying anything. . . . I was with somebody and I was moving out. . . . I was with a spirit or angel or I don't know. Somebody else will have to name my companion. . . . I was right with it. (I–65)

A visually perceived spiritual being appeared during fifteen NDEs. In half of these cases, this spirit was identified as a deceased relative, who characteristically appeared happy, content and in good health. Such was the case with one 43-year-old man during his postoperative cardiac arrest and NDE:

> I came to some place and there were all my relatives, my grandmother, my grandfather, my father, my uncle who had recently committed suicide. They all came towards me and greeted me. . . . My grandparents were dressed . . . all in white and they had a hood over their heads. . . . They looked better than the last time I saw them . . . very, very happy. . . . I held hands with my grandmother. . . . It seems like I had just come up on them and they raised their heads up and they were all happy. . . . And all of a sudden they turned their back on me and walked away and my grandmother looked over her shoulder and she said, "We'll see you later, but not this time." (I–44)

Another survivor of a cardiac arrest encountered healthy-appearing relatives known to be dead at the time:

> My grandmother had been ninety-six. She never did look old, she

looked perhaps forty or forty-five. My mother was sixty when she died and way overweight, and she looked trim and a good general-health look, happy and healthy [during the NDE]. Everybody looked healthy, real, real healthy. (I–57)

Two people felt as if they had looked into the face of the Lord. A 55-year-old Protestant Florida woman recalled this encounter in the following way:

Just as clear and plain the Lord came and stood and held his hands out for me. Well, he stood there and looked down at me and it was all bright then. . . . He was tall with his hands out and he had all white on, like he had a white robe on. . . . It [the face] was more beautiful than anything you've ever seen. His face was beautiful, really and truly beautiful. His skin was almost like it was glowing and it was flawless, absolutely flawless. . . . He just looked down at me and kind of smiled because he had just appeared, holding his hands out. (I–41)

The vision of another person or being could not be definitely identified in five cases. A 54-year-old Illinois salesman was met by two unidentified men during his NDE in 1976:

First of all, two men met me and they showed me such respect, such high regard, like I was an admiral in the navy. They called me by my name. They had been waiting for me. It just seemed so real that I immediately knew that I had passed on. . . . They said, "We're here to show you the way." I said, "All right." I started walking with them. . . . These two men had a terrific sense of humor. They made jokes about different things as we were walking and made it very light. . . . They were both dressed the same, like a khaki uniform, but that's kind of hazy. . . . They said, "You shouldn't go back. It's too hard for you to go back now." I said, "No. I really want to. . . ." They said, "We don't wish to be abrupt, but we're going to have to be on with it. If you do not wish to go, we've got to get on. Don't be concerned. We'll be back for you." (I–52)

Finally, combinations of religious figures and deceased acquaintances were included in the descriptions of four NDEs. For example, a sixty-year-old Protestant man from Florida was confronted by both his deceased mother and Christ during a cardiac arrest in January 1975:

I could see Mother and Christ just saying, "Come on home. Come on home." They were waving their hands at me at the same time.

... She [his mother] was tall, had a long sparkling silver gown on, and so did Christ. That is, I took it to be Christ, long hair and what have you. Long beard. . . . They were both smiling. Very happy.. . . [It was] just like I was talking with them myself. . . . I could hear them. (I–25)

Life Review

Only two persons reported a rapid mental replay of significant past life events during the NDE. This life review was described by the man whose case was presented at the beginning of this chapter:

During this stage, my life just flashed in front of my face. My whole life. . . . Things that had happened to me in my lifetime, like when we got married, just flashed in front of my eyes, flashed and it was gone. When we . . . had our first child flashed in front of my eyes. The biggest thing, I guess, and the longest thing that stayed flashing in front of my eyes, was when I accepted Jesus Christ. (I–15)

The other life review was encountered by the aforementioned Vietnam veteran while he was lying wounded on the battlefield:

When I came down and hit the ground [after being blown up by the explosion], I remember sitting up and I saw my right arm gone and my right leg gone and my left leg was laying off to the left side. I fell back . . . and my whole life was just going in front of me like a very fast computer and I kept thinking about all the different things I had done or perhaps I hadn't done. (I–68)

In each of these cases, the life review was a very early event in the overall NDE and probably began prior to full loss of consciousness. This suggests that the life review may at times occur separately from the other elements of the NDE, which develop *after* the onset of unconsciousness.

The Return

Since the transcendental NDE was perceived as having taken place outside the physical body, the experience necessarily ended with a feeling of having returned to this body. In the majority of cases, this "return" was either influenced or directed by another spiritual being (see Table XIII). That is, "communication" took place between the person near death and these other spiritual beings, with the life-death issue involved in some way. This communication was later identified as an important reason for the person's return to life.

Other people felt as if a strong, unidentified force had actually drawn them back into their physical body. A 60-year-old man described this force as a giant magnet:

> This force started drawing me back [to my body] like a giant magnet. A force stronger than anything we know. I resisted it with all my force and strength to stay, but there was no way. Then everything went completely black. (I-57)

A woman was "pushed back" from her NDE by an unidentified "something":

> I was trying to get there but something kept pushing me back. ... I got to drifting back ... and I just came floating back down to my body. (I-17)

A "border" or "limit" within the transcendental environment was occasionally perceived as representing the point of no return. Passage over this limit, it was felt, would have resulted in irreversible bodily death. At times, this "border" was identified as part of the transcendental environment itself, and included a stream of water: "I've almost gotten across ... a still stream of water ... but they seem to push me back and tell me it's not time yet" (I-18); a barbed-wire fence: "And something told me that if I banked, as an airplane would bank, to the right and didn't stay right over that fence, I'd be gone. I wouldn't come back. And I seemed to say to myself that I would like to see my wife some more and I would like to fish some more. And then I came to at about that point" (I-47); and a mountaintop: "And a voice, a clear voice, said, 'You can't go yet. You have unfinished business. Fall this way, don't fall the other way.' And I rolled over and fell on the left side of the mountain. That was the end and I woke up. ... [Do you feel if you had rolled over to the right side you wouldn't be here?] Yes, that's right." (I-54)

This border or limit was described by some persons as being the outstretched hands of a visualized spirit present during the transcendental experience. These people felt that if only they had reached these hands they would not have come back. A 67-year-old woman yearned to reach the outstretched arms of her deceased husband as he was wading across a stream to meet her:

> S: My deceased husband was coming with outstretched arms in the water and I was coming too. He was coming after me. ...

A: What do you think would have happened if you had taken your husband's hands up there?

S: I think he would have carried me on across.

A   Would you have come back?

S: No.

A: Did you want to [go across] at the time?

S: Yes, I was so eager to see him.

A: What kept you from going on ?

S: I don't know. If it had been my decision, I guess I would have gone on. . . . I feel like I'm left here for some reason. (I–34)

Finally, the "return" from the transcendental experience was for some an unexpected, spontaneous event which seemingly interrupted the flow of the experience in midstream. In the midst of one transcendental NDE, "all of a sudden everything just blacked out" (I–25) for a 60-year-old man following his cardiac arrest. A 32-year-old man described a similar ending: "Some part of me was going . . . but it didn't go. . . . [Suddenly] I was back down and the doctors and nurses were all around." (I–4)

The Combined Near-Death Experience

So far, we have examined the autoscopic and transcendental elements found in the NDEs reported by persons in this study. While 33 percent of these NDEs contained *only* autoscopic elements and 48 percent contained *only* transcendental elements, 19 percent contained elements of *both* (see Table VIII). In these combined NDEs, the transcendental portion of the experience followed the autoscopic portion in a continuous, unbroken sequence. The following clinical vignette from my own practice will serve to illustrate the combined NDE:

August 1977. I encountered in the ear, nose and throat ward of the Gainesville VA Hospital a patient who had suffered a severe automobile accident several years before. He was in the hospital at this time for treatment of a chronic severe ear infection which had persisted since his skull was fractured during the accident. I met him in his room and he was quite willing to talk.

He took me back to May 1970, when he was in his late forties, working as an executive field supervisor for a large company. On the twenty-third of that month, he was walking home from a friend's house late at night. At 1:10 A.M. (according to police records), he was crossing a street when he was struck from behind by a speeding vehicle which had apparently gone out of control. After being hit, he remained conscious but unable to move. The driver of the car stopped and backed up to see what he had hit. In the process, he ran over the man a second time, rendering him unconscious. The next thing he recalled was waking up in great pain in the hospital, several days later. This is his account of what took place during this period of unconsciousness.

When I was in the emergency room I seemed to be there but then I wasn't there. . . . I seemed to see myself on this gurney or whatever, and they moved me to a table. . . . I seemed to be one of the participants in there, but back farther from the table than anyone else . . . in the background. . . . I was able to look down . . . I was able to see all this. . . . The table was over like at that end of the room and the doctors were on the right side of me and they had a lot of nurses on the left side. There was also a priest there. . . . They didn't have to give me pain shots or anything, because I was completely out of it. . . . I just kept saying, "That isn't me." But I knew it was me and that something had happened. . . . I thought the whole thing was strange; I had never experienced anything like it. . . . I wasn't frightened in the least. . . . I was all black from the road tar. . . . I had cuts all over my face that were all bleeding. I remember the way the leg was, all the blood; I remember one doctor saying, "He is going to lose his leg. . . ." In the meantime they gave me a tourniquet on my leg. . . . The monitor was at the back of my head, in the back of me. . . . I was able to see the line on the monitor . . . and all of a sudden it stopped and it looked like a TV tube when you reset the tube . . . you see that green line go across and it made one continuous noise. . . . Then I heard somebody say, "It's stopped," or something like that . . . and I remember one of the doctors banging on my chest, pushing on it. . . . That's when they brought this unit out . . . they were rubbing those things together . . . and I was there all this time and I thought: My God, this can't be me. . . . I came off the table about nine to ten inches. . . . I seemed to arch . . . and then I was in complete, total darkness. . . . I went through this period of darkness. . . . There was this light, like someone holding a flashlight, and I started going towards that. And then the whole thing brightened up and the next thing I remember was I was floating. . . . We were going through this shaft of light. . . . The light kept getting brighter and brighter. . . . It was so bright, and the closer we

got, the brighter it got, and it was blinding. . . . I had angels around
me. . . . But the angels around me were all my children. My oldest
son was seventeen at the time but yet he was in the lead and I
couldn't get over it because he was like around six years old. All my
children were at my side, three on one side, three on another side,
and my son was in front of me. . . . They were all almost the same
age. . . . I think it has something to do with the most favorite time I
have had with my children in my life. . . . I remembered when I
used to have tea parties with [my oldest daughter] . . . when she was
a little girl. . . . My older boy, I remember being downstairs and I
think we were building a bookcase and he was talking to me about
something he wanted to do. . . . But with each of the children something came back to me which was the most favorite, most intimate
time I had had with them. Something with each of them that struck
me personally. . . . There was no communication between them and
myself. But when I looked at them I associated each one with something in the past . . . I seen a lot of beautiful blue . . . on all sides of
us was this beautiful blue. You can't even call it a sky, but it was a
deep blue . . . a beautiful color. I've never seen a blue like that. . . . I
felt a very slight pressure on my head and I heard a voice say, "Go
back!" . . . I said, "Why me, Lord?" and whoever spoke said my
work on earth wasn't over yet, that I had to go back to complete it.
. . . All I heard was his voice; it was loud, thundering, just like a
clap of thunder coming out of nowheres. . . . [After that] I don't remember anything, the children leaving me, the blackness, or nothing. I only remember waking up in intensive care two days later.
(I–8)

This man's medical records indicated that he had indeed been admitted that night with multiple skull and leg fractures and had suffered
a cardiac arrest while being evaluated in the emergency room. Subsequently, he had been admitted many times for various complications
which have resulted from the original trauma.

Thus we have seen that two types of vivid experiences may be encountered at the point of near death—the autoscopic and the transcendental. But who are the people who have described these encounters;
what are their social, educational, occupational and religious backgrounds? What circumstances of the near-death crisis events seem to
have precipitated these experiences? These questions and more will be
addressed in the next chapter.

5

Analysis of the Data

AT THE BEGINNING of this study, Sarah Kreutziger and I set out to answer six basic questions about the near-death experience which had arisen out of Raymond Moody's book, *Life After Life*. As noted in Chapter 1, these questions were:

1. Was the NDE as described by Moody actually occurring in our own patients who had survived an episode of unconsciousness and near death?

2. Did these NDEs follow a consistent pattern or patterns?

3. How often were NDEs occurring in persons revived from a close brush with death?

4. What were the backgrounds of the persons reporting an NDE and what were the medical circumstances under which they occurred?

5. Did the content of the NDE vary between groups with different backgrounds or between groups with different near-death situations?

6. Did the NDE per se affect the person's death anxiety or afterlife beliefs?

The first two of these questions have been answered in the preceding two chapters: the NDE was found clearly to occur in patients while unconscious and near death and to follow three consistent patterns: the autoscopic, the transcendental and a combination of the two. The remaining four questions are considered below.

How Often Does the NDE Occur?

In *Life After Life,* Moody presented the NDE based on "approximately" 150 cases which he had encountered in the course of his work. Most if not all of these cases had been referred to him from a variety of sources. In considering these "referred" cases, we are not able to assess the frequency of occurrence of the NDE, since all of Moody's interviews were with persons who had had the experience. To determine the frequency of occurrence of the NDE among survivors of a near-death event, a group of near-death survivors would have to be interviewed without the interviewer's knowing whether or not an NDE had been encountered. The frequency of occurrence of the NDE could then be determined by comparing the number of persons reporting an NDE with the total number of near-death survivors interviewed.

In this study, 116 persons who had survived a near-death crisis event were interviewed (see Table I). Ten of these persons had encountered their crisis event while under general anesthesia for a major surgical operation. Since we defined the near-death crisis event as any episode of unconsciousness *associated with* physical near-death and since the unconsciousness during the surgical operation was associated (at least in part) with the general anesthesia, the surgical crisis events would not fully meet the criteria established for a near-death crisis event, even though the surgical complication may in itself have been a life-threatening event. Thus the NDEs associated with a surgical complication are presented separately in Chapter 6, "Surgical Experiences," and are not included in the following analyses.

Having excluded the ten surgical cases in this study, we are left with 106 cases of a near-death crisis event. Of these 106 cases, 78 were obtained in a prospective fashion (see page 6). The only information known about these 78 persons prior to the interview was that each had survived at least one nonsurgical episode of unconsciousness and near-death. These episodes included 66 cardiac arrests, 8 comas and 4 life-threatening accidents (see Table IV). Of these 78 prospectively interviewed patients, 27 (i.e., 35 percent) had encountered multiple near-death crisis events during their lifetime (see Table VII). When more than one crisis event was reported by the same individual, the most recent event or that associated with an NDE was chosen for analysis.

Of the 78, 34 (43 percent) reported an NDE following a near-death crisis event. Since some of these persons had had multiple crisis events, the *estimated total** of near-death crisis events that had occurred in the lives of these 78 persons was 156. Some persons had also encountered more than one NDE in their life, raising the *total* number of NDEs reported by these persons from 34 to 42. Thus the approximate incidence of NDEs *per near-death crisis event* in the lives of these 78 persons was 27 percent (42 NDEs occurring during 156 near-death crisis events). From this, we can say that the NDE is a *common* experience among persons surviving an episode of unconsciousness and near-death.

The NDE—*Who* Has It and Under *What Circumstances?*

Other questions that arose out of *Life After Life* concerned the personal characteristics of individuals reporting the NDE and the circumstances under which the NDE occurred. In particular, since all persons do not report an NDE following a near-death crisis event, are there differences in the social and demographic backgrounds of those who do and do not report the experience? To determine this, each person's age, sex, race, area of residence, size of home community, education, occupation, religion, frequency of church attendance, and previous knowledge of the NDE were evaluated (Table II). Using these variables, comparisons were made between groups with and without an NDE. No significant differences were found between the groups with and without an NDE except in the area of previous knowledge of the NDE. Significantly fewer persons with an NDE claimed to have had knowledge of the phenomenon prior to their near-death crisis event than persons without an NDE. The reason for this finding is unclear. One possible explanation may involve the time at which the near-death crisis event occurred. On the average, the crisis events of persons without an NDE occurred 1.3 years prior to the interview (see Table IV), whereas the crisis events of persons with an NDE occurred an average of 4.9 years before the interview. That is, the crisis events of the "nonexperiencers" were more recent than those of persons experiencing an NDE. Publicity concerning the NDE has only lately become quite widespread. It is possible that this publicity played a role in "informing" many persons with a recent crisis event about the NDE prior to their own near-death crisis event. This, in

---

* In a few cases, multiple cardiac arrests or other crises events had occurred separately during hospitalizations many years ago. If all the medical records could not be obtained, a conservative estimate of the total number of crisis events was arrived at from the testimony of the interviewee and others (relatives, etc.) present at the time.

turn, may account for the difference as to "previous knowledge of the NDE" between persons with more recent and remote near-death crisis events. Whatever the explanation may be, these findings suggest that an awareness of the NDE does not seem to predispose persons to having such an experience, since, in this study, those with "previous knowledge" reported the experience less frequently following their close brush with death than those without such "previous knowledge."

What, then, are the circumstances under which these NDEs occurred? Do the details of the near-death crisis event differ in persons with and without an NDE? To answer this question, the circumstances of each near-death crisis event were adduced from both the medical record and the person's own recollection. First, the crisis events were divided into three categories: cardiac arrest, coma and accident. Second, the *location* of each crisis event was determined as being either in or out of a hospital environment. Third, an estimate of the *duration of unconsciousness* associated with each near-death crisis event was made (when more exact information was not available from the medical record) in the following manner: (1) *less than one minute* to include very transient cardiac rhythm disturbances, causing a brief loss of consciousness and usually not requiring any resuscitative measures; (2) *one to thirty minutes* to include most cardiac resuscitations, unless prolonged or extenuating circumstances were known to have been present (i.e., repeated unsuccessful defibrillations followed by eventual restoration of cardiac rhythm); and (3) *greater than thirty minutes* to include most comatose situations. Fourth, the *method of resuscitation* was evaluated in each case, using the following scheme: (1) *none* to include persons recovering without any assistance; (2) *medications* to include all "nonelectrical" methods and drugs commonly employed in an acute medical crisis (i.e., external cardiac massage, medications to normalize cardiac rhythm and to maintain blood pressure, etc.); (3) *medications plus defibrillation* to include all methods in category 2 plus defibrillation (an electrical shock applied to the chest to correct a potentially fatal cardiac rhythm disturbance); and (4) *chronic supportive* to include all support measures (i.e., intravenous glucose, electrolytes, antibiotics, etc.) used in critical, nonacute comatose situations.

A comparison of the groups with and without an NDE as to the circumstances of the near-death crisis is found in Table VI. The type of crisis event was similar in both groups. However, the group with an NDE more frequently encountered their near-death crisis event within a hospital, were more commonly unconscious for greater than one minute, and more often received some type of resuscitative measure than persons without an NDE. In evaluating these findings, it should be kept in mind that 85 percent of this entire group of 78 persons were survivors of a cardiac arrest. In general, persons treated for an in-hospital cardiac arrest will be more likely to survive an arrest that persists longer than one minute and will be more likely to receive some type of resuscitative measure than persons encountering similar arrest situations out of the hospital. This would account for the appearance of all three of these cardiac arrest variables—(1) location in a hospital; (2) unconsciousness lasting greater than one minute; and (3) involvement of some method of resuscitation—together in the same group. The fact that all three of these variables were found more frequently in cases with an NDE, however, suggests that arrests associated with an NDE may be of a more serious nature (i.e., closer to death?) than arrest situations not associated with an NDE.

Does the Content of the NDE Vary Between Groups with Different Backgrounds or Between Groups with Different Near-Death Situations?

So far, comparisons have been made between groups with and without an NDE as to the background characteristics of the near-death survivor and the circumstances of his near-death crisis event. The next question that might be asked is whether the *content* of the NDE is affected by the person's background or mode of near-death.

Table IX presents the ten elements of the NDE along with their frequency of occurrence in the overall group of 61 NDEs. These elements were discussed at length in Chapters 3 and 4. Do these elements vary significantly in the NDE reports of persons with different backgrounds? As can be seen in Table X, no significant differences in the occurrence of these elements were found between groups broken down according to age, area of residence, size of home community, religious background or frequency of church attendance. Moreover, groups with the highest and lowest levels of educational attainment reported these elements with similar frequency.

When the person's sex was considered, it was found that females more often reported element 9 ("encountering others") than their male counterparts. In addition, this same element appeared more frequently in the laborer-services occupational group than in the group of professionals.

Generally, these findings indicate that the content of the NDE is quite consistent among near-death survivors from the American culture with differing backgrounds. The statistically more frequent occurrence of element 9 among females and persons in the laborer-services group is a finding for which I have no ready explanation. These statistical differences, however, should be confirmed in future studies using a larger sampling size, to ensure that the findings are not merely chance occurrences among a large number of comparisons involving relatively small population groups.

Does the occurrence of these ten elements vary with the circumstances of the near-death crisis event? The results summarized in Table XI indicate that no significant differences were found between groups broken down according to type of crisis event, estimated length of unconsciousness and method of resuscitation. In addition, the time that had elapsed between the crisis event and the interview did not seem to affect the content of the NDE, since interviews conducted within one month of the crisis event produced elements of the NDE that were similar to those found in interviews occurring five years or more following the crisis event.

Does the NDE Affect the Person's
Death Anxiety or Afterlife Beliefs?

Moody noted in *Life After Life* that most persons who had encountered an NDE had "lost" their fear of death. It is unclear from his work, however, whether this decrease in death anxiety was a result of the NDE per se or of having successfully survived a close brush with death—that is, having somehow "beaten the odds." Would persons resuscitated from a near-death crisis event without an NDE express similar changes in their fear of death?

To answer this question, each person in this study was asked to assess the effect, if any, that their near-death crisis event (with or without an associated NDE) had on their fear of death and their afterlife beliefs. Responses to these questions were grouped into three categories: a definite increase, a definite decrease, or no change in the respective attitude or belief. The results of this questioning are presented in Table XIV. A definite decrease in the fear of death and a definite increase in the belief in an afterlife were reported by the vast majority of persons with an NDE—a response significantly different from that of persons surviving similar near-death crisis events without an NDE. This indicates that the decrease in the fear of death following an NDE is due to the NDE per se, and is not a result of merely having survived a near-death crisis event.

The death anxieties of persons surviving a near-death crisis event (with or without an associated NDE) were further evaluated using the Templer and the Dickstein death anxiety scales. These scales, which have been validated in the psychological literature to measure death anxiety, were mailed in 1978 to all persons who had been interviewed in the study up to that time. Forty-four persons returned these death anxiety scales—twenty-six who had had an NDE and eighteen who had not had an NDE associated with their near-death crisis event. The results are presented in Table XV. The group with an NDE scored significantly lower (indicating less death anxiety) on both the Templer and the Dickstein scales than the group without an NDE. These findings coincide with those found at the initial interview—that is, that (1) the death anxieties of persons reporting an NDE are lower than those of persons without an NDE and (2) the persons reporting an NDE claim that their lower death anxiety is an aftereffect of their NDE.

Summary

The data presented in this chapter indicate that the NDE is a common experience encountered by persons during a near-death crisis event. In this study, it was found to occur in approximately 40 percent of prospectively interviewed near-death survivors. A person's age, sex, race, area of residence, size of home community, years of education, occupation, religious background or frequency of church attendance did not seem to affect whether he or she would or would not encounter an NDE during a near-death crisis event. Moreover, knowledge of the NDE prior to the near-death crisis event did not appear to predispose the person subsequently to report an NDE following a crisis event.

The type of near-death crisis event (i.e., cardiac arrest, coma or accident) did not affect whether or not an NDE would occur. Reports of NDEs were more common, however, following in-hospital near-death crisis events associated with unconsciousness for longer than one minute and involving some type of resuscitative measure.

The content of the NDE based on the ten elements was, in general, quite consistent between groups with varying social and demographic backgrounds. However, females and persons in the laborer-services occupational group more often reported element 9 ("encountering others") than males and professionals. The content of the NDE also was consistent between groups with differing circumstances of the near-death crisis.

Following the near-death crisis event, persons with an NDE claimed a decrease in their death anxiety and an increase in their afterlife beliefs—a response quite different from that given by survivors without an NDE. Moreover, this difference in the death anxieties of persons with and without an NDE was substantiated by the Templer and the Dickstein death anxiety scales.

6

Surgical Experiences

WHEN WE DEVISED our study, Sarah and I planned to interview all patients who were mentally stable and were known to have survived a near-death crisis event. We defined this near-death event as any bodily state that caused physical unconsciousness and would reasonably be expected to result in irreversible biological death if urgent medical attention was not given. Persons who had recovered from a life-threatening surgical complication which had occurred in the midst of a major operation were included in our interview group and were approached in the same manner as the others. Later, however, we realized that it would be impossible to determine whether unconsciousness in the surgical situation was a result of the near-death crisis event per se or of the general anesthetic administered. For example, was the massive hemorrhage associated with the inadvertent laceration of the spleen during the elective nephrectomy (removal of kidney) in Interview 51s (see Table V) severe enough to cause physical unconsciousness in an otherwise awake individual? We simply could not tell. We had to conclude that a surgical crisis event could not safely be considered a near-death crisis event as defined in our study. Thus we removed all such surgical experiences from the overall group of NDEs and considered them separately. As it turned out, these cases offered a unique opportunity to "verify" the autoscopic aspects of the experience.

In all, thirteen experiences were described to us (see Table V) by persons who had recovered from a major operation. The type of surgery and the circumstances under which the experience occurred varied widely. In fact, three experiences were reported following surgical operations in which *no* known complications had taken place. The content of these experiences were quite similar, however, to nonsurgically related NDEs. Both autoscopic and transcendental encounters were reported. Many patients described the progress of their surgery as they "saw" it from a point above their bodies. In these cases, comparisons could be made between the patient's account and the operative summary dictated by the attending surgeon. As this chapter reveals, there were some amazing similarities.

The Autoscopic Surgical Experience

Four persons claimed to have "observed" their operation from the ceiling of the operating room. One such case was reported by a cardiac patient shortly following an open-heart operation at the University of Florida in January 1978. This man, a 52-year-old night watchman from rural north Florida, had had two previous heart attacks with cardiac arrests, in 1973 and 1975. He was first referred to the university hospital in November 1977, for cardiac catheterization and evaluation for surgery, at which time I met him. He told me of an extensive autoscopic NDE he had had during his first cardiac arrest. The details of this interview are found on pages 25–26 and 87–88. I continued to follow him through his open-heart surgery in January 1978. Following his surgery, he alluded to some type of experience he had had during his operation, but was reluctant to discuss it for fear of discrediting his account of his previous NDE. This recent experience, he said, was too much for me to swallow. I convinced him that I wanted to hear about it anyway, so he reluctantly related the following operative recollections:

> The anesthesiologist deadened this area and put a thing [IV] there. . . . I must have dozed off to sleep. . . . When I left that room [prior to surgery], I was totally unconscious and don't have any awareness whatsoever as I was transported from there down to where they do the operation until all of a sudden the room is lit up, not as bright as I thought it ought to be. Then I became aware but, in fact, they

had already done some stuff to me. They had finished draping me, the anesthesiologist had started his stuff, and all of a sudden I became aware of it . . . like I was in the room a couple of feet or so above my head, like I was another person in the room. . . . It was like I would think of something and I would see, in color and in a frame, what I wanted. I recall consciously . . . seeing two doctors stitch me up after the operation; Dr. C, I think it was because the hands were so large, injecting a syringe of something into my heart on two occasions, one on one side and another on the other side of the heart; the apparatus that they used to keep the ribs apart to make the aperture; some apparatus they put in this vein up here, some kind of readings that they were taking, an instrument up there; something shiny in his hand—that was the anesthesiologist, I'm sure of that. I couldn't see it all. And the fact that my head was covered and the rest of my body was draped with more than one sheet, separate sheets laid in layers. I knew it was my body. I always imagined that the lights would be brighter, but it didn't seem that bright. More like banks of fluorescent lights rather than a big high-powered beam. . . . I can remember parts of the conversation that went on in there and that surprised me. . . . They had all kinds of instruments stuck in that aperture. I think they're called clamps, clamped all over the place. I was amazed that I had thought there would be blood all over the place, but there really wasn't that much blood. Not what I expected it to be. . . . Somehow or another I was able to realize what was going on like I was looking from back behind my head. It's kind of scary in that I don't know why I should be able to do that. But I know what I saw. It's authentic, or rather I believe it is. . . . A lot of it was draped. I couldn't see my head too much but I could see from about my nipples down better. . . . I was out of my body. . . . [Sewing him up] they took some stitches inside me first before they did the outside. And then it was just like they sew you up. The shorter doctor started down here and worked this way. The other doctor could have started in the middle and worked up. They had a lot of trouble right here, but the rest of it was pretty fast. . . . And the heart doesn't look like I thought it did. It's big. And this is after the doctor had taken little pieces of it off. It's not shaped like I thought it would be. My heart was shaped something like the continent of Africa, with it being larger up here and tapered down. Bean-shaped is another way you could describe it. Maybe mine is odd-shaped. . . . [The surface was] pinkish and yellow. I thought the yellow part was fat tissue or something. Yucky, kind of. One general area to the right or left was darker than the rest instead of all being the same color. . . . I could draw you a picture of the saw they used and the thing they used to separate the ribs with. It was always there and I can remember the details of that probably better than the other things. It was draped all around, but you could see the metal part of it. I think all they used that for was to keep it constantly open. They had instruments hanging around it that obscured it and they undid the clamps sometimes and stuck in sponges stuck on the clamps and there were hands so I couldn't see it constantly because it was obscured sometimes. . . . It seems Dr. C did most everything from my left side. He cut pieces of my heart off. He raised it and twisted it this way and that way and took quite a bit of time examining it and looking at different things. They even looked at some of the arteries and veins and there was a big discussion on whether they should do the bypass up here. No, I guess it would be over here, because I thought the heart was over here [to the left] but it's more centered here [midline]. And they decided not to do that. It seems that I have an overly large vein that made itself bigger and supplies plenty of blood and I could hear them discussing that. . . . This sounds weird, but I wasn't concerned. . . . I didn't feel like I was going to die. I had a lot of confidence in Dr. C. He really is an impressive sort of fella. . . . That thing they held my chest open with, that's real good steel with no rust, I mean, no discoloration. Real good, hard, shiny metal. . . . [Stopping his heart] I sense they did it with the needle when they injected something into my heart. That's scary when you see that thing go right into your heart. . . . I was real curious but I wouldn't want to ask any of the doctors on that team because it would be stupid, I guess. All but one doctor had scuffs tied around his shoes and this joker had on white shoes which had blood all over them. I was wondering why this one doctor was in a pair of patent-leather white shoes in the operating room when the nurses and everybody had green covers that they put their shoes into and it was tied. . . . I'm morbidly curious about that. It seemed so odd. . . . I thought it was unsanitary. I don't know where he had been walking in those things, but it upset me. I thought he ought to be covered like everybody else. . . . And there was a doctor who had a bad little finger and it looked like he was going to lose his nail. There was a blood clot under his fingernail on his right hand. I could see it through his gloves, which were more or less transparent. It was real dark and I recognized it for what it was. He was the one who did the stitching and was on the opposite side of the table from Dr. C. (I-19s)

At the end of this description of his surgical experience, I asked him to compare it with the NDE he had had during his cardiac arrest in 1973.

But this is distinctly different from the time I had the cardiac arrest ... the feeling. In the first experience [cardiac arrest] I died—I mean, what there was left of me, whether it was my brain, my soul, my spirit. That's a different feeling. This is more earthly, just like I had two feet planted on the ground. I could sense things like I was consciously aware of them. . . . I don't think I died like I died before.

How, then, does this description of an open-heart operation by a lay individual from rural north Florida compare with the actual procedure as described by the surgeon in charge? From the operative report (which had never been made available to the patient), I found the following description:

A satisfactory general anesthesia [halothane] was introduced with the patient in the supine position. . . . He was prepped from the chin to below the ankles and draped in the customary sterile fashion. . . . A long midline incision was made extending from just above the sternal notch to below the xiphoid [lower part of breastbone], carried down sharply through the skin and subcutaneous tissue. Hemostasis was carried out. . . . The sternum was sawed open in the midline, a self-retaining retractor was utilized over wound towels. . . . [After the heart had been exposed] Two 32 Argyle venous lines were placed through stab wounds in the right atrium [heart chamber]. . . . One of these tubes extended into the inferior vena cava and one into the superior vena cava [large veins which feed blood to venous side of heart]. . . . The patient was placed on cardiopulmonary bypass. . . . The ventricular aneurysm [large scarred area of heart which represented area of previous heart attack and would have appeared to be of a different color than the normal heart muscle that remained] was dissected free. . . . The aneurysm was seen to be very large. . . . An incision was made over the most prominent portion of the aneurysm after the heart had been turned upside down in the pericardial wall. . . . The entire aneurysm was resected [cut away]. . . . The left ventricle was then closed. . . . Air was evacuated from the left ventricle with a needle and syringe. . . . An attempt to wean the patient from cardiopulmonary bypass was unsuccessful on two occasions. . . . The patient then gradually began to recover and was able to maintain satisfactory function. . . . The wound was closed in layers. . . . The pectoral fascia [chest muscle attachments] was reapproximated with interrupted sutures of 2-0 Tevdek . . . subcutaneous tissue was closed with a running suture of 3-0 chromic . . . the skin was closed with 4-0 nylon. . . . The patient was sent to the Surgical Intensive Care Unit in stable but critical condition. . . . Time operation began 0910 . . . time operation completed 1220.

The surgeon's description of this man's operation contains many specific details which were also described by the patient, as if he had visually witnessed the procedure. A comparison of some of these details taken from the two accounts of the same operation follows:

PATIENT'S DESCRIPTION	SURGEON'S DESCRIPTION
1 "my head was covered and the rest of my body was draped with more than one sheet, separate sheets laid in layers."	1 "draped in the customary sterile fashion."
2 "I could draw you a picture of the saw they used."	2 "The sternum was sawed open in the midline"
3 "the thing they used to separate the ribs with. It was always there. . . It was draped all around but you could see the metal part of it.. . . That thing they held my chest open with, that's real good steel with no rust, I mean, no discoloration. Real good, hard, shiny metal."	3 "a self-retaining retractor was utilized over wound towels."
4 "One general area to the right or left was darker than the rest instead of all being the same color."	4 "the ventricular aneurysm was dissected free. . . . The aneurysm was seen to be very large."
5 "He cut pieces of my heart off. He raised it and twisted it this way and that way and took quite a bit of time examining it and looking at different things."	5 "An incision was made over the most prominent portion of the aneurysm after the heart had been turned upside down in the pericardial wall. . . . The entire aneurysm was resected."

6 "injected something into my heart. That's scary when you see that thing go right into your heart."

6 "Air was evacuated from the left ventricle with a needle and syringe."

7 "they took some stitches inside me first before they did the outside."

7 "the wound was closed in layers. . . . The pectoral fascia was reapproximated with interrupted sutures of 2-0 Tevdek . . . subcutaneous tissue was closed with a running suture of 3-0 chromic . . . the skin was closed with 4-0 nylon."

The patient's description contains, in addition, many details and "visual" impressions that were not commented on by the surgeon in his report because such details were not essential or appropriate in an operative summary. It is important to point out, however, that these additional observations made by the patient are accurate within the general context of open-heart operations. For instance, the patient's description of the shape and consistency of his heart after his chest had been opened is a classic.

In another case, a 42-year-old woman from Missouri described to me her lumbar disk surgery as if she had watched it from the ceiling of the operating room. Her experience, which took place in September 1972, unfolded as follows:

[On the morning of surgery] they had given me some sort of shot and I was really sleepy anyway. I don't remember going out of my room to the operating room. . . . What I recall while I was in the operating room was it seems like I was just floating up near the ceiling. It seemed there was a light over my shoulder because it was really warm. I guessed that was the operating table light or something like that. I felt really good and I was really excited about what they were doing. . . . It was sort of a funny feeling because I was up there and this body was below. . . . It was a green room. One of the things that struck me was I thought that they would have the operating table parallel to where all the instruments are but it was actually at an angle in the room. I thought that was really interesting. . . . They had surgical gowns on. . . . I could see them operating on my back. I was just sort of floating there. It occurs to me now that I wonder why I wasn't sick watching an operation. I remember noticing one doctor on one side of the table and the other was, I later found out, the chief resident in neurosurgery; he was on the other side. Seems like the chief resident was doing a lot more of the surgery than Dr. D. He was sort of telling him where and so forth. I thought that was interesting because the other guy [Dr. D] was supposed to be doing the surgery. Then I remember Dr. D saying, "There's the disk. There it is." At that point, I came down closer to see what was going to happen. I came right down to the operation and I was amazed how deep my spine was in my back and how many layers with things clamped and all sorts of stuff. It was really incredible how deep my spine was. I had thought it was right on the surface. Then I saw them reach in, I guess it was on my left-hand side, and get the disk out . . . it seemed like they had a long pair of tweezers but angled at the end, with which they actually removed the disk. . . . I got the feeling this was absolutely fantastic. I kept saying to myself, "That's really incredible! That's really amazing!" I was just amazed at how they did it and how quickly. Just then somebody up by my head said—uh—I can't remember the words because they were kind of technical, but I knew what the word meant at the time and it was stopping breathing or something like that. "Arresting," I think he said, "arresting." He said "close" and all of a sudden they started pulling out clamps real fast out of my back and closing up my skin. I was still down close to the operation and they started sewing up from the bottom. They were sewing up so fast that when they got up to the top there was a gaping piece of skin on my back. I was really annoyed because they had just pulled the one piece of skin too hard, I guess. I was thinking: I could have done better than that. But I guess I couldn't have done it as fast. At that point it was no longer very interesting, so I floated up to the ceiling and out the door and down the hall. I was really close to the ceiling, because the fluorescent lights were really bright. I don't remember anything after that until I woke up looking up in a different room. It was dark outside and I thought they had really operated early in the morning because it was still dark, but it was nighttime. And this other doctor, I recognized him and I hadn't seen him before the operation. He was the one doing most of the surgery. I knew who he was when I saw him. I asked him what was wrong and he said, "We can't get your heartbeat regulated." I said, "Well, would it make a difference if I had rheumatic fever when I was young?" And he got mad and said a few words and said, "Why didn't you tell us?" I guess I went back to sleep. . . . Afterwards when they took the bandage off and I got to look at the operation, there was a big gaping hole at the top. I could see where they had sewn it up. On the left-hand side they'd pulled the skin too much and there was a gaping place there, 'cause 'I remember complaining to them. . . . And when I was talking to the nurse and a couple of things I'd said about the operating room and where the window was and the door being right across from it, the table being on an angle and it being a green room, over to my left there was a table along the wall that had all the instruments on it— she said that was right because she was a student nurse and had been in the operating room a lot. . . . I said that I recalled that this resident was doing most of the surgery and she checked with some other nurses and they verified the things that had happened. . . . Everything I saw was too accurate. I really did see what was there. (I–70s)

This woman's hospital records indicated that two physicians were in the operating room performing the surgery—the attending surgeon (Dr. D) and the chief resident in neurosurgery. The attending surgeon dictated the following operative summary at the end of the case:

> With the patient in the prone position, the usual midline incision was made [in the back]. Skin edges were retracted and deep fascia [tissue] was divided. Muscle stripped off the spines and laminae [parts of the vertebral bones in the spine] of L4-5 and S-1 [indicates the level of the operation on the spinal column]. . . . After removing a small amount of lamina of L5, I was able to locate a large mass of completely extruded [ruptured] disk. . . . This huge fragment was lying free in the canal and was removed. Following this . . . a large amount of self-degenerated disk material was removed from within its space. . . . The wound was . . . closed tightly in layers with interrupted fine silk sutures. . . . The patient returned to the recovery room . . . [with] a few premature ventricular contractions [cardiac irregularity]. For this reason, monitoring was continued in the recovery room.

After the woman had been transferred to the recovery room, an emergency internal medicine consult was obtained to treat the cardiac irregularity that had begun in the operating room. This cardiac irregularity subsided spontaneously shortly thereafter and the remainder of the hospital course was uneventful.

In comparing the accounts of the surgery given by the patient and the surgeon, no inconsistencies could be found. It is of particular interest to note the woman's annoyance at having "seen" the chief resident in neurosurgery—whom she "hadn't seen . . . before the operation"—perform a major part of the surgery. Apparently she had been led to believe

that her attending surgeon (Dr. D) would be the primary operating surgeon. Then, when this resident physician first visited her in the postoperative recovery room, she claimed to have recognized him as the one
"doing most of the surgery." The hospital records seemingly verify this
aspect of the woman's story, since the only notes on the chart prior to
surgery were written by Dr. D. Following the operation, however, daily
progress notes by the chief resident could be found until the woman's
discharge from the hospital.

I interviewed the "student nurse" to whom this woman described
her experience. Although this nurse had forgotten many details of this
conversation, which had occurred six years previously, she could definitely recall the following information:

> Mainly what I remember was that she had some kind of arrhyth-
> mia or something. She told me that she remembered people saying,
> "Hurry up, we've got to finish the procedure [surgery]." She had
> something like an out-of-body experience. . . . She remembered the
> bright light and that they hurried up to close her back up. . . . I
> remember her saying something like the scar was uneven or some-
> thing like that.

Thus this woman's description of her surgical "out-of-body" experience appears, at least in part, to be substantiated by available hospital
records and a nurse who was present. Whether the autoscopic experience was related in any way to the cardiac dysrhythmia that appeared
late in the operation is difficult to tell. From the woman's testimony,
however, it appears that the experience began well before the onset of
the cardiac difficulty.

A third surgical autoscopic experience started a bit differently from
the preceding two cases. On the morning of May 29, 1969, a 22-year-old
American soldier suffered severe injuries from a "booby trap explosion"
near Cu Chi in Vietnam. Unconscious and in profound shock, he was
taken by helicopter to the 12th Evacuation Hospital and was immediately rushed into the first available operating room for life-saving surgery.
This man's NDE began on the battlefield at the time of the initial explosion and continued on into the surgical procedure. The surgical portion of the experience is excerpted below:

> The whole time I'm looking at my body it was always from the
> upper left. I always seemed fixed in that position. I was above the
> head of the highest person. . . . They picked me up and run me in

[to the operating room]. . . . I remember them sticking a tube down my mouth—the air tube or anesthesia tube or whatever. I don't remember the sensation of going under like the feeling you have during an operation. That definitely did not happen. . . . At the beginning [of the operation] I saw them cut my uniform off and start whatever fluid they have to start. At that time my left leg was cut off. It was only hanging on by a piece of skin. . . . I saw them cut the rest of it off. At that time I had a knee also. It was right below the knee where they cut it off. . . . I remember this scar here [on forehead]—when they sewed this up. I had an open wound here which they sewed up. Plus the one on my left arm—I remember them sewing that up. . . . As far as the conversation in the operating room, I couldn't tell you what they said. . . . I know they were talking but I can't remember what they said. Most of the perception was in sight, if that's what it's called. . . . I couldn't understand why they were doing what they were doing. . . . I really believe that I was dead. . . I actually remember grabbing the doctor. . . . Nothing [happened]. Absolutely nothing. It was almost like he wasn't there. I grabbed and he wasn't there or either I just went through him or whatever. [After regaining consciousness] I perceived who I was talking to although I was laying in bed. I knew it was the nurse and doctor who had operated on me. I knew the doctor's voice when I heard it, even though they didn't know that I knew them. . . . I had no eyesight for about three weeks. I literally could not open my eyes. I had bandages on them to start with. They had been singed and burned. (I–68s)

This man's military medical records from Vietnam were recovered and documented the following events:

This 22-year-old white male captain stepped on a booby trap at 0858 hours, 29 May 69 near Cu Chi in the Republic of Viet Nam. He sustained traumatic amputation of the right arm at the humeral joint [shoulder] with transection of the axillary artery and vein and the brachial plexus [severance of all blood and nerve supply to arm]. He also sustained traumatic amputation of both legs. Bilateral perforation of tympanic membranes [eardrums] with hearing loss was also inflicted from booby trap explosion along with open lacerations over trunk, face and left upper extremity without nerve or artery involvement. He was taken to the 12 Evacuation Hospital and arrived there at 0940 hours in shock with no blood pressure. Cut down [surgical incision to locate a vein for intravenous administration of medications] was done stat [immediately] and the first of nine units [pints] of blood was begun. Patient taken immediately to operating room and intubated [placement of tube into windpipe] and given Sodium Pentothal, nitrous oxide and oxygen for general anesthesia at 1000 hours. Blood pressure at beginning of procedure was 65/38. Surgery consisted of right shoulder disarticulation, left knee disarticulation and right above the knee amputation. Despite the administration of over 12 liters of blood and fluids, the patient remained hypotensive [low blood pressure] throughout surgery, with the pressure dropping as low as 62/28. Surgery completed at 1315 hours with blood pressure 80/40. After surgery, patient noted to be extremely restless and agitated but gradually regained consciousness and convalesced. On 3 June 69 the patient was evacuated to 106th General Hospital where several operations had to be performed to revise the wounds. On 16 June 69 he was evacuated to Fort Gordon, Georgia, for further treatment and rehabilitation.

The final autoscopic surgical experience was reported by a 37-year-old Florida housewife who had had two previous autoscopic NDEs during nonsurgical near-death crisis events. Her surgical experience occurred during an elective gall bladder operation with no known complications. She places heavy emphasis on her auditory perceptions during the operation and quite likely was in a light plane of anesthesia ("They didn't know how I had awakened so soon [after the operation]"). Nevertheless, she describes definite "visual" perceptions of parts of the operative procedure, as if looking down on it from above:

I had been concerned about the surgery and I was determined that they were not going to take my consciousness away from me, that somehow I was going to be aware of what was going on. I had thought about this a great deal before going in. That I was going to watch and see everything that was going on. They started the IV and gave me Sodium Pentothal and I was drifting off to sleep. He said count and I got to about three and went to sleep. Then this other part of me, whatever it is, again was looking down from a height and watching them prepare me. The surgeon came in. But with the medicine [anesthesia] I couldn't see as I had before [during NDE]. I was like watching a television set and at times just static— the whole picture going or sound being muffled. At times I could see very clearly and see what they were doing, hear some of the things that were going on. But most of the time it was just in and out. I caught some of their conversation about a golf game—some of the personal chatter and some parts of the operation. . . . I could see my body lying there. One thing that struck me was that I could remember going in and getting on the table before they put me to sleep and how cold it was in there. Then when I was looking down I was thinking: Well, it doesn't feel cold anymore. It feels comfort-

able. But I could remember the difference because I had felt so cold
physically. I was icy cold in there. Well, to me it was like being in a
balcony looking down watching a movie or something going on. I
saw them cut me open. I saw blood. You don't feel anything. It
doesn't hurt. It's a very calm feeling. You just see what's going on
but you don't feel anything that's physically done to your body. But
I couldn't see everything and hear everything. Somehow with the
medicine, as hard as I was concentrating—I guess in my own mind
I was afraid I was not going to live through the surgery—somehow
I felt if I can keep control, they couldn't take my consciousness
away from me. This is what had been in back of my mind. But the
medicine did interfere an awful lot with it. I woke up immediately
[after the operation] and I helped slide from the operating table
back to the cart. They didn't know how I had awakened so soon.
They told me I was supposed to sleep for an hour or so after the
surgery. But I woke up immediately as soon as they stopped operating and they were transferring me over to the cart and I helped
slide back onto the cart. It was the anesthesiologist that had made
the remark about his golf game and that's when I was looking
down. I was asking him about his golf. He just laughed and said,
"How in the world did you hear that?" I said, "I don't know." He
pushed me back to intensive care and I was drowsy but I never did
go back to sleep. I was back to me again and talking to the girls in
the recovery room. (I–28s)

The Transcendental Surgical Experience

Nine patients described a transcendental pattern for their surgical experience. This pattern was identical to that in reports of nonsurgical survivors of near-death crisis events. None of these persons had encountered
an NDE prior to their surgical experience. One such experience was
reported by a 48-year-old cardiac patient of mine. This man had undergone an open-heart operation in August 1975. His description of this
surgery follows:

> [Prior to the surgery] There had been several other guys there [in
> the room] who had had the surgery and they were telling me about
> it and we were laughing a lot. I was telling them jokes and they just
> begged me to stop because it made them laugh so hard that it hurt
> their chests [from the surgical incision]. . . . And I didn't have any
> fear at the time. . . . I went into the surgery with no fear, absolutely
> no fear whatsoever. . . . The day the surgery was scheduled they

gave me the necessary shots to give the "Don't care" feeling . . . no coffee or cigarettes that morning. . . . And I was just laying in there [operating room] with no clothes on and there was this beautiful woman in there and I was worried about whether they would keep me covered. And she spread my two little fingers apart and stuck a needle in my hand and that's the last thing I remember until they were waking me up and taking a tube out. [At this point] I was remembering things that had happened and I was thinking about this death experience. I was walking across this wooden bridge over this running beautiful stream of water and on the opposite side I was looking and there was Christ and he was standing with a very white robe. He had jet-black hair and a very black short beard. His teeth were extremely white and his eyes were blue, very blue.. . . He looked different from any pictures I had seen before . . . I was not afraid but was very much at peace and I wanted to make sure that I was really there. . . . It's real . . . very real to me. . . . I knew very well that I had died. Nobody had to tell me, I knew. . . . And as I got closer and closer I tried to detect everything in order to convince myself that this was indeed Christ waiting on me. And I looked at his hands and there were the scars where the nails had gone through. And as I was looking, trying to convince myself that this was really Christ, there was no conversation. The only thing I had was total, complete peace.. . . As time passed on, I knew it wasn't my time to go with him. He was smiling and turning me in a direction to cross back over this little bridge. . . . It was just a handmade, wooden type walk-across bridge. . . . As I was walking, I was looking back and I was really wanting to go with him. And I gradually crossed over to the other side. . . . It was the side of a hill, very green with a rock or two here or there. A stream was coming down with nice clear water—just a real peaceful, beautiful setting. The sky I can't recall seeing, or paying that much attention to it. My real focus was on the white robe and if I could prove it to myself that this was really Christ. . . . And all during this time the knowledge, the universal knowledge, opened up to me and I wanted to capture all of this so that when I was able, I could let people know what was really around them. Only trouble was that I was unable to bring any of it back. . . . I really wanted to capture all of this in my mind. I wanted to grasp it all. In fact, I wanted to tell my wife about it. I really wanted to bring it back. . . . And the next day or so after they had taken me out of that first intensive care room my wife came in to visit me and looked at me and said, "You have the bluest eyes, the bluest eyes" and I told her without thinking that I had looked into the eyes of Christ. And I said this automatically and I didn't know exactly what I should have said but it came out.... She really didn't know what I was talking about.... I knew without ever questioning him [the doctor] that I had gone. And then I started trying to figure out if any of the other guys had had such an experience during their operation. I couldn't find anybody that had.... About two years after this I was reading that book *Life After Life,* and several of those experiences were about the same. (I–71s)

I interviewed this man's wife and she remembered very well her surprise at hearing her husband say on the second postoperative day that he had "seen Christ." Two or three days later, he told her about the whole experience. She knew then that her husband had required resuscitation from a cardiac arrest at the end of his surgery. She insisted, however, that *he* was not aware of this complication at the time and had specifically not been told because of his unstable medical condition. In fact, she recalled her husband's surprise two months later when, while waiting to see a doctor, he had inadvertently been left with his medical chart and had read for the first time about the cardiac arrest. His words at the time: "Damn! I didn't know I had died in Birmingham [where the surgery had been done]."

The medical details of his open-heart operation and cardiac arrest were quite clear from the chart:

> Anesthesia [halothane, nitrous oxide] was begun at 2 P.M. Patient placed on cardiopulmonary bypass at 4:03 P.M. Three saphenous vein aorto-coronary bypasses were performed without difficulty. Patient off cardiopulmonary bypass at 6:02 P.M. At 6:30 P.M. patient suffered marked hypotensive episode [low blood pressure] followed by ventricular fibrillation [cardiac arrest] requiring intracardiac epinephrine and two countershocks [electric shock to heart]. Patient reverted to normal rhythm but electrocardiogram indicated new injury pattern [heart attack]. Patient taken to recovery room in "fairly good condition" at 8 P.M.

Several post-surgical notes in the chart made reference to the cardiac arrest and heart attack during the operation. It was probably one of these notes that caught this man's eye two months later when he was reading through his chart. Thus it appears that he had a transcendental-type experience while under general anesthesia and reported the experience to his wife shortly after the surgery, at a time when he himself was unaware that an intraoperative complication and cardiac arrest had occurred.

Another transcendental encounter was reported by a man who had been admitted to the hospital in shock from a leaking abdominal aortic aneurysm. Sometime during surgery, he had the following experience, which was "the only memory I carried for eight days in intensive care" after the operation:

[During surgery] Here comes this white light. It didn't blind me. It was just the whitest white and the total area was filled with it. . . . It was just like you looked out into a total universe and there was nothing but a white light. The most brilliant thing in the world, and it was not the kind of white that hurt a person's eyes like looking at a light bulb. . . . Then I said to myself as plainly as I'm saying to you, "So I'm dying. I don't want to, but I'm not going to fight it. If this is death, I'll accept it." I had a very, very pleasant feeling. There was no panic on my part, no apprehension. It was a very pleasant thing. Now I saw nobody, but I just had this talk with myself, just knowing that: Hey, you're dying. You're not ready but you're not going to fight it. . . . [Later] I thought: Gee, what a horrible dream that was. But it wasn't a dream. It was too real and it happened. So two months and thirteen days later I saw my doctor again and he said, "You're very special to me." I said, "Why is that?" and he said, "Well, you know you totally died. We lost all life signs while you were on the operating table." I said, "Yes, I know it, Doc!" He said, "You do?" and I said, "I remember dying." (I–55s)

The medical records and operative report tell the following story:

This 59-year-old white male . . . was brought to the emergency room. . . . He was found to have hypotension [low blood pressure] and the skin was found to be cold and clammy. . . . Patient continued to be complaining of back pain . . . appears pale, but he is alert and cooperative. . . . Impression: Dissecting and leaking abdominal aortic aneurysm. . . . Plan: Immediate surgery. . . . Under general anesthesia [surgery was completed]. . . . His blood pressure, which was 40/0 at the start of the operation, was 160/80 at the conclusion. . . . During the procedure the patient received seven units [pints] of whole blood transfusions. . . . Transferred to recovery room in good condition.

Several reports in the medical literature have described the experiences of anesthetized patients who have recounted an awareness of ongoing surgical events. This phenomenon was discussed in the October 6, 1975, issue of the *Journal of the American Medical Association* (*JAMA*) by Dr. Richard S. Blacher, in an article entitled "On Awakening Paralyzed During Surgery—A Syndrome of Traumatic Neurosis." Dr. Blacher interviewed patients who had reported an actual awakening from light anesthesia during a major operation and who had been unable to move at the time from the generalized paralysis which had been medically induced by a commonly used muscle relaxant. These patients presented a characteristic syndrome following their surgical experience, consisting of: "(1) repetitive nightmares, (2) generalized irritability and anxiety, (3) a preoccupation with death, and (4) difficulty . . . in discussing their symptoms, lest they be thought insane."[1] In each of these cases, the patient emphasized the *unpleasantness* of the situation—"of being tied down and unable to move"—and a reliving of this experience through "recurrent nightmares of waking in pain and being paralyzed." Only one patient was reported to have remembered specific details of the operative procedure—a woman who "recalled her surgeon giving orders."

In reply to Dr. Blacher's article, several letters were published in the March 22, 1976, issue of *JAMA*. These letters supported Dr. Blacher's findings and added descriptions of a number of "dreams" which had been reported by other patients under similar situations. One physician wrote that a patient of his had told him that "the operation was terrible! So painful, like a nightmare." He went on to say that this patient "also recalled people and conversations from the operating room, although this was mixed with more dream-like images also involving her teaching colleagues and conversations with them from the day before surgery."[2]

Another letter dealt with a physician's own experience:

> Nearly everyone has had a bad dream of trying to run away from some form of danger, but being unable to move. The dream usually ends with the sleeper waking. Though I was not asleep [during surgery] I endured the same terror, but the "dream" would not end. The sense of helplessness seemed to go on forever.[3]

In comparing this "Syndrome of Traumatic Neurosis" encountered by inadequately anesthetized surgical patients to the thirteen surgical experiences found in this chapter, several differences are evident. In the *JAMA* reports, neither the calm and peaceful feeling of the transcendental surgical experience nor the detailed "visual" observations of the autoscopic surgical experience were described. Moreover, the "dreams" of the persons in the *JAMA* articles had the flavor of ordinary dreams and nightmares—that is, the content was variable and "dream-like" (e.g., recent "conversations" with "teaching colleagues," "trying to run away from some form of danger"). The content of the transcendental surgical experience, on the other hand, followed the typical pattern of an NDE and was later perceived by the person as non-dream-like reality.

Investigations into patient awareness of intraoperative events have been conducted by Dr. David Cheek and others. These physicians have based their work on the premise that memories of operating room experience are stored by the patient's subconscious mind and often cannot be reached using ordinary conversational technique. To probe these subconscious memories, a large number of patients have been hypnotized following general anesthesia for a major surgical procedure and have been regressed back to the time of the operation. As reported in the January 1960 issue of the *Rocky Mountain Medical Journal:*

> From the evidence so far available, it seems true that the hearing sense is maintained to depths of clinical intoxication beyond that at which all other perceptions and all commonly tested reflexes are suppressed. . . . Details are recalled *only* when *the spoken words* [italics mine] have been frightening, or have relieved anxiety related to the surgical experience.[4]

Thus recollections of words spoken during the surgical procedure can later be retrieved from the subconscious mind of many anesthetized patients. However, operative details that can only be visualized, not heard (the shape and surface appearance of the heart, the appearance of the surgical instruments used in the procedure, etc.), were not found in the recollections of Dr. Cheek's hypnotized patients.

In sum, the experiences presented in this chapter occurred under a variety of surgical circumstances, three of them during operations in which no life-threatening complications were recorded in the medical record. In content and quality they closely resemble the nonsurgical NDE. They bear no resemblance to the nightmarish experiences often reported by inadequately anesthetized patients. *Visual* details of an operation are not later retrievable by hypnosis from the subconscious minds of patients who had been anesthetized, although *spoken* words sometimes can be recalled. Furthermore, the "visualized" details of the autoscopic experience closely match the actual operative procedure performed by the surgeon. Thus any consideration of possible explanations for the NDE must take into account these surgical experiences, which, to all intents and purposes, appear identical to their nonsurgical counterparts.

7

The Autoscopic Near-Death Experience: Fact or Fantasy?

IT WAS ON the morning of June 6, 1966, about five o'clock in the morning. . . . We could pretty much see the Viet Cong in the tree line, which must have been about three hundred feet away. For us, we must have been thirty-five men at the time. They began shooting a few mortars, along with a whole lot of machine gun fire. We were able to see a couple of machine guns and the guy about three down from me had a light antitank rocket which was called a LAR, that you put on your shoulder in the manner of a bazooka. The guy who was in charge of the infantry at the time told him to see if he could knock out the machine gun. As he got into position to do so, he was hit instantly. . . . Just as I was about to get up to knock him down to change the direction of that rocket I was first hit right between my thumb and the rest of my hand. By the time I shook that off and I was about to start back up, the rocket went off and exploded. At that time I can recall doing a somersault to the rear as a result of the concussion. . . . Just as I landed and was able to shake my head, a mortar landed behind me and I did a somersault forward. That was about it until it appeared to be about a couple of hours later. . . . I could see the VC. I could see the guy that pulled my boots off. I could see the rest of them around picking up various things. They were taking rings. . . . It was like I was looking right down on it right now. I could see me. . . . It was just like I was looking at a manikin laying down there. . . . I could see my face and I could see my arm. I was pretty well burnt up and there was blood all over the place. . . . I could see an M-14 [rifle] about three or four feet away, and I was trying to get to it, but I just could not move. . . . It was like being in a deep dream. . . . When the guy was at my boots, I could see that and at the same time it was like waiting for him to get through so when he turned his attention I could get to my rifle, but I couldn't get my body to move. . . . It wasn't as if I could feel a broken leg or an amputation or a twisted back or something like that. It was just that I couldn't get that *manikin* to get to the rifle. . . . I was trying to get that physical manikin over there to get that weapon. I was like a *spectator* . . . like it was happening to someone else. . . . It was about four or five in the afternoon when our own troops came. I could hear and see them too. . . . It was quite obvious I was out of it, burnt up. All the top part of my garment was burnt off too. I looked dead. . . . They put me in a bag. . . . We were piled up on the amtrac. . . . If I had seen any of them [the soldiers] afterwards, I would have been able to recognize them. . . . We were transferred to a truck and then taken out to the morgue. And from that point, it was the embalming process. I then remember being on that table and that guy telling a couple of jokes about those USO girls. . . . All I had on at that time was bloody undershorts. [I watched as] he just snatched those off and he placed my leg out and cut [into the left groin to expose the femoral vein to inject the embalming fluid]. . . . He had already made a slight incision and when he stopped to laugh, he was just curious as to why there was that degree of blood. So he checked my pulse and heartbeat again and I could see that too, standing up about as if you were looking at a third party. . . . He checked the pulse, and he wasn't sure so he asked someone else. He had decided that he would stop cutting at that point. It was about at that point I just lost track of what was taking place. . . . They apparently took me to another room and severed my hand off and maybe a few minutes after that surgical procedure, the chaplain was in there saying everything was going to be all right. . . . I was no longer outside looking at the situation. I was part of it at that point. (I–69)

As this man was telling me his story, one question kept running through my mind: Could this really have happened as he had described it? It was apparent that at least a portion of his account could be correct—he was wearing a prosthetic right arm. But what could be said of his alleged trip to the morgue in a bag? I asked to examine his left groin. There I found additional support for his story—a well-healed scar over his left femoral vein, consistent with the incision from an embalmer's knife. These bits of evidence suggested to me that his story *might be* correct, but further verification was not possible because of the circumstances of his case. Thus other NDE cases would have to be examined if I was to determine, as I had set out to do, whether autoscopic NDE events are fact or fantasy.

I had known from the beginning of my study that the majority of the patients I would be interviewing regarding the NDE would have been resuscitated from cardiac arrests. At this stage in my career, I had personally directed and participated in well over a hundred such procedures. I knew what a resuscitation consisted of and how it would appear to an onlooker. I had been eagerly awaiting the moment when a patient would claim to have "seen" what had taken place during his resuscitation. Upon such an encounter, I had intended to probe meticulously for details which would not ordinarily be known to nonmedical personnel. In essence, I would pit both my experience as a trained cardiologist and the description of the resuscitation in the medical chart against the professed visual recollections of a lay individual. Thus, I was convinced, obvious inconsistencies would appear which would reduce these "visual" observations to no more than "educated guesses."

Five years later, thirty-two survivors of a nonsurgical crisis event who had claimed to have "seen" portions of their own resuscitation had been interviewed. As I prepared to analyze the results I wondered just *what* would comprise an "educated guess" on these matters. Did these thirty-two people have sufficient knowledge of the resuscitation procedure prior to their NDE to construct a plausible approximation of their near-death crisis even without having observed it from their purported out-of-body location?

Most of these NDEs focused on the recollection of events that had occurred during cardiopulmonary resuscitation (CPR) for a cardiac arrest. Now, I knew that no two CPR situations would appear exactly alike. I also knew, however, that there is a general procedure for CPR which is followed by trained hospital personnel. A person familiar with this CPR protocol might be able to reconstruct a believable version of the events of his own resuscitation.

The majority of people reporting an autoscopic recollection of their own cardiac arrest situation were "seasoned" cardiac patients who had had multiple exposures to the equipment and procedures used in modern intensive care unit facilities. They had *been* there. Moreover, their awareness of their own chronic cardiac condition might have made them more attentive than the average person to CPR protocol portrayed on television, in movies, and the like. In assessing their level of knowledge of CPR procedures apart from their autoscopic NDE, it would have been ideal to have interviewed each person prior to his NDE. However, all persons in this study were interviewed after their near-death crisis event. During this "post-event" interview, each person with an autoscopic recollection of CPR was asked to comment on his familiarity with this procedure prior to his NDE. Many admitted that they had previously viewed television programs or other reenactments of CPR which may or may not have resembled details witnessed during their own autoscopic experience. Others maintained that they had never seen such a procedure other than at the time of their own near-death crisis event. Such retrospective assessments of prior knowledge of CPR are open to question, however, since the person was being asked to evaluate the level of his own prior knowledge in the absence of any objective documentation. To circumvent this problem partially, an indirect measure of prior CPR knowledge was obtained in the following way:

Twenty-five "control" patients were interviewed whose backgrounds were similar to those reporting autoscopic NDEs (see Table III) and who had been consecutively admitted to a coronary care unit (CCU). These twenty-five controls were seasoned cardiac patients with an average duration of known heart disease exceeding five years, including prior cardiac-related hospitalizations for a heart attack (20 patients), heart catheterization (12 patients), open-heart surgery (8 patients), elective cardioversion (2 patients), cardiac arrest without an NDE (4 patients) and cardiac pacemaker implantation (1 patient). While in the CCU, each of these patients had had the opportunity to observe closely at his bedside a cardiac monitor to which he was attached, a cardiac defibrillator, and intravenous needles and equipment. Moreover, each patient had admitted to regular viewing of a home television set prior to this admission. Thus this group of twenty-five cardiac patients had received considerable exposure to hospital routine and television programs, both of which could have contributed to their knowledge of CPR.

During the interview, each patient was asked to imagine that he was standing in the corner of a hospital room watching a medical team revive a person whose heart had stopped beating. He was then asked to describe in *visual* detail what he would expect to see in such a situation. He was cautioned to describe only those details that he was reasonably confident would actually be seen during CPR on a hospitalized patient. Each of these interviews was tape-recorded and later analyzed.

Twenty-three of the twenty-five interviewed patients made some attempt to describe the CPR procedure based on their own general knowledge of hospital equipment and protocol. Without undue prompting, twenty of these twenty-three respondents made a major error in their descriptive accounts. The most common error was the belief that mouth-to-mouth breathing would be the routine method of artificial ventilation in the cardiac-arrested, hospitalized patient. In truth, mouth-to-mouth breathing is a rarely used means to oxygenate a patient during in-hospital CPR because of the rapid availability of alternate, more efficient methods of artificial respiration* (see autoscopic descriptions of CPR later in this chapter).

Additional errors in these descriptive accounts included misconceptions (by separate patients) of the oral airway used to ensure an open air passage during CPR ("They would use wooden throat paddles, like an ice cream stick, only bigger"); misconceptions of cardiac massage ("a blow to the back to start the heart beating again," "opening up the chest to place the hands around the heart and massage it," "a hard blow to the solar plexus to get the heart started again," "the doctor doing the pushing on the chest would straddle the patient over his thigh region and push up"); misconceptions of cardiac defibrillation ("electric shock would be given through those wires which are fastened onto the chest and hooked up to the cardiac monitor," "the electric shock would be given through a needle stuck in the heart through the chest"); and misconceptions about the defibrillator paddles used to deliver the electrical energy to the chest ("they would be hooked up to an air tank and pressurized," "they would have a suction cup on the bottom of them," or "they would not be hooked up to anything").

Three of the twenty-five patients gave *limited* descriptions of CPR procedure which were without obvious error. One patient was able to describe the cardiac defibrillator present in his room at the time of the interview ("that machine over there") but had no concept of the technique of external cardiac massage, artificial ventilation or other CPR procedures. Another patient had watched his father's resuscitation in a

---

* I suspect that this concept of mouth-to-mouth breathing as a frequently used *in-hospital* technique has arisen from television programs and movies which portray *out-of-hospital* resuscitations where mouth-to-mouth ventilation is the only means available.

hospital emergency room and recalled the following scene: a "doctor pushing down on his [father's] chest, center of the chest, with one hand on top of another and sweat pouring off" and "something going in his [father's] arm, with a nurse holding up some sort of liquid in a bottle." The third patient had watched his roommate being resuscitated in the surgical intensive care unit during a previous hospital admission: "the doctor was pressing down on the chest, one hand over another" and the defibrillator was "a big square machine with two pad-looking things with wires on them." This last patient was unable to describe how those "two pad-looking things" would be used on the patient and did not comment on artificial ventilation or use of needles or injections.

To summarize the results of this control study, twenty of twenty-five cardiac patients made a major error in their descriptive account of in-hospital CPR, three gave a limited but correct description, and two claimed no knowledge of CPR technique whatsoever. The backgrounds of these patients were similar to those of persons describing this same CPR procedure based on an autoscopic NDE. Thus the results of this control study offer us some insight into what an "educated guess" would be when based on a cardiac patient's prior general knowledge. Let us keep this in mind as we turn, now, to the actual autoscopic NDE descriptions of in-hospital CPR.

Autoscopic Descriptions with Nonspecific Details

Twenty-six of the thirty-two autoscopic descriptions contained only *general* "visual" impressions of the near-death crisis event. Verifiable details could not be recalled despite specific questioning (e.g., "Did the doctors or nurses do anything else to your head, face, mouth or chest during your resuscitation? Did they use any machines or equipment, needles or injection?"). This inability to recall verifiable details was attributed by the person, time and time again, to the fact that his attention had been directed toward the unique and pleasant qualities of the experience, in overall amazement at what was occurring, and not toward the physical events themselves. It was as if the procedural aspects of the resuscitation took on secondary importance:

> I was standing in the doorway. It was a room similar to this except, if I recall correctly, there was a window. Yes, I'm sure there was. The lights were on and there was this group there that took care of me. And in this bed was a person who I know must have been me. . . . I was on a level with them. The doctor that was working on me, he

didn't have on any white coat, just his shirt. There was another one there that was dressed in white and he was a man around fifty. There were two nurses there, and I got a good look at one of them. . . . I really didn't pay too much attention to them. It was a feeling of freedom that I had. The serenity, the buoyancy of it. . . . I was fascinated. (I–23)

Each of these twenty-six nonspecific autoscopic descriptions *did* correspond in a general way to the known facts of the near-death crisis event. It is difficult to analyze the accuracy of these accounts, however, solely on the basis of content. Nevertheless, it should be noted that when control patients with similar backgrounds were asked to reconstruct in-hospital CPR, fully 80 percent made at least one major error—in matters about which they had been "reasonably confident" they were correct. Such errors of commission were not present in the nonspecific autoscopic accounts, leading me to believe that these NDE accounts most likely are not subtle fabrications based on prior general knowledge. However, this reasoning is tenuous, at best, and needs the support of a more detailed analysis of the content, per se, of the autoscopic NDE.

Autoscopic Descriptions with Specific Details

Six of the thirty-two persons describing an autoscopic NDE were able to recall specific details of their near-death crisis event. How well, then, do the events mentioned in the patient's description match the actual situation as reconstructed from the known facts in each case?

CASE 1

Mr. P (I–19) was a 52-year-old security guard from rural north Florida at the time of our interview in November 1977. He had had a massive heart attack associated with a cardiac arrest in the emergency room of a Florida hospital in December 1973. He had never been hospitalized previously for cardiac problems. His recollection of this cardiac arrest is as follows:

S: I couldn't stand the pain anymore. It was increasingly getting worse. So I got up and started out of the hospital. I just have little spots of memory on this. And then I collapsed. That's when everything went dark, and I don't remember anything else except it was like I was just fainting at the beginning. Just

like pulling a curtain or snapping a light or something. Everything went black. After a little while, it was not black but there
was no light. It was kind of like a gray fog. I don't know how
else to describe it. It wasn't real dark like midnight, but I
couldn't see any point of light. Then I could sense a lot of
activity going on. Somewhere around that point, I was still on
the floor, but I saw me. I thought how unusual it was, I was
sitting up there somewhere and I could look down, and I had
never noticed that the floor was black and white tile. That's the
first thing I remember being conscious of. I guess I got more
light because I could see black and almost off-white tile. And I
recognized myself down there sort of curled around in a half-
fetal position. Two or three people lifted me and put me up on
a tray, not a tray but a dolly, all metal with four legs. They
strapped my legs and started me moving back in the general
direction where I had come from. We got down there, and they
turned me facing down the main hall. It was at that point I
noticed another table-like arrangement with a bunch of stuff
on it. I know it later to be the machine that they thump you
with. We were going to meet—Bear in mind, I'm not a drug
user. I don't take trips and I've never tripped out on anything
like that. This is no figment of my imagination. I've never read
on this subject. . . .

A: How did you feel when you were in that state?
S: Pretty good, buoyant. I thought: Gee, here's something going
    on that nobody else knows about. . . .
A: When you were looking down, could you see details?
S: Yes. I could see a whole lot of details, like blood spots on the
    wall where some feller's arteries were open and had splattered
    up on the wall and no one had washed it up.
A: Could you see your face?
S: I could see my right ear and this side of my face because I was
    facing away.
A: And the cart they were wheeling down the hall?
S: Yes. That was making a terrible racket. That caught my atten-
    tion right away.
A: Did you watch as they thumped you?
S: Yes. The first time.
A: What did that look like?

S: In what way?

A: Could you describe the sequence of events of how they thumped you?

S: I thought they had given my body too much voltage. Man, my body jumped about two feet off the table. After that first shock and by the time they had administered a second one, I got back in my body. . . .

A: From where you were, could you see the monitor?

S: It was like an oscilloscope. Just a faint white line, running, with a little fuzz dropping down at the bottom. It seemed like fuzz, but it seemed more like a straight line. It wasn't a big monitor like when they put the TV monitor on you in the cardiac cath room. This thing was only about an eight-inch envelope. It made the same streak, over and over. . . .

A: Where about did they put those paddles on your chest?

S: Well, they weren't paddles, Doctor. They were round disks with a handle on them. No paddles. They put one up here, I think it was larger than the other one, and they put one down here.

A: Did they do anything to your chest before they put those things on your chest?

S: They put a needle in me. I thought at the time it looked like one of those Aztec Indian rituals where they take the virgin's heart out. They took it two-handed—I thought that was very unusual—and shoved it into my chest like that. He took the heel of his hand and his thumb and shot it home. I thought that was very unusual.

A: Did they do anything else to your chest before they shocked you?

S: Not them. But the other doctor, when they first threw me up on the table, struck me. And I mean he really whacked the hell out of me. He came back with his fist from way behind his head and he hit me right in the center of my chest. And then they were pushing on my chest like artificial respiration, not exactly like that but kinda like artificial respiration. They shoved a plastic tube like you put in an oil can, they shoved that in my mouth.

A: Did they try to start an IV?

S: Yes. They tried to start one in my left hand, but my hand had been fractured in the door. Then they went over and they put a long paddle, and the paddle was up underneath the table. They stuck that out and then they started one on the back of my hand. But I'm sure that was after, after the monitor started registering heartbeats and I had gotten back in my body.

A: Had you ever seen on TV a similar sequence of events?

S: No. But after I got out of the hospital, they had a program called *Emergency*. I watched that and in one of the segments, they had a cardiac arrest on the concrete in the street. I started watching it, but I couldn't watch it because I got real severe chest pains just watching it. I had to get up and leave and take a nitroglycerin. My wife won't even let me look at it. But I only saw the first part, where they rip open a man's shirt.

In summary, this man reconstructed the following events from his autoscopic NDE: his body being lifted off the floor onto a stretcher; his legs being strapped to the stretcher; a sharp blow to his chest by a "doctor," followed by manual chest compression; his body being wheeled down the ER hall on the stretcher to meet the emergency cart with the defibrillator, cardiac monitor and other resuscitative equipment; the insertion of a plastic airway into his mouth; the cardiac monitor; the injection of medications into his heart; two attempts at cardiac defibrillation and the regaining of physical consciousness, after which an intravenous line was started in the back of his right hand.

Comment: The emergency room records (which had not been made available to this man) indicated that he had arrived at the hospital at 7:43 P.M., complaining of severe chest pain. This pain was initially diagnosed as a hiatal hernia, a painful gastric disorder. He was given some pain medication and released to home. While leaving the ER at 9:35 P.M., he suddenly collapsed in the hall. He was immediately found to have no pulse or respiration and CPR was begun. Several cardiac medications were administered. Two 400 watt-second defibrillations (electric shocks to chest) were delivered for ventricular fibrillation (heart stoppage), after which the man regained consciousness. He was then admitted to the intensive care unit of the hospital with a final diagnosis of an acute myocardial infarction (heart attack) and cardiac arrest.

This man's autoscopic description of his cardiac arrest and CPR correlates well with the medical account recorded in his chart. As is usual in such cases, the medical record summarized only a portion of the details of the CPR procedure (the type and dose of cardiac medications, type of cardiac dysrhythmia, electrical defibrillation, etc.). The man's account, however, described in procedural detail how the CPR had been performed. His description is extremely accurate in portraying the appearance of both the technique of CPR and the proper sequence in which this technique is performed—i.e., chest thump, external cardiac massage, airway insertion, administration of medications and defibrillation.

The injection of cardiac medications directly into the heart was not specifically mentioned in the ER records, however. This procedure is not commonly performed today during in-hospital CPR, but was common practice in the early 1970s, when this man's cardiac arrest occurred. It is a rapid (and at times dangerous) method of administering cardiac drugs when no other intravenous route is immediately available. In this man's situation, he most certainly did not have an IV in place at the time he was stricken, since he was on his way home. Moreover, from his own description, he recalls an IV being started in his right hand *after* resuscitation. It is quite likely, then, that direct-to-the-heart medications were given during the urgent circumstances of his cardiac arrest and that a regular IV was started at a later time.

Following our interview, I came to know this man quite well and visited him several times at his home. At no time did I find any indication that he possessed more than a layman's knowledge of medicine. Moreover, from the flow of our initial conversation during the interview itself (which was unplanned and unrehearsed), it is evident that many of the details he recalled were given in response to my own probings and were not volunteered, as might have been expected from an informed individual attempting to "reconstruct" the events of the resuscitation from a detailed knowledge of the procedure. I was also struck by his reaction to my inadvertent use of the word "paddle" to describe the instrument that is held on a patient's chest during electrical defibrillation. "Paddle" is a widely used term for these instruments and is so ingrained in my mind that I use it without thinking. The man demonstrated his unfamiliarity with this word, however, by his response: "they weren't paddles, Doctor. They were round disks with a handle on them. No paddles." His description is quite accurate, of course, in a literal sense. His reaction, however, was but one more clue that he was not conversant with common hospital terminology and procedure, especially as it applies to CPR.

CASE 2

Mrs. M (I–45–2) was a 60-year-old housewife at the time of our interview in August 1978. She had been hospitalized on the neurosurgical

service in January 1978, for severe back strain. While awaiting break-
fast one morning in her hospital bed, she suffered an episode of unconsciousness and profound shock, presumably from a cardiac arrest. She
reported "seeing" the following events during this episode:

S: All of a sudden I felt very strange, and I glanced at the door,
and the nurse was there, and I said, "Something's wrong," and
that's the last I remember. She [later] said when she got to the
bed, I had no pulse, no respiration, no nothing. I had left my
body and was to the side in sort of like a tube. . . . I saw them
doing all this stuff to me. . . .

A: You could see what they were doing to your body at the time?

S: Yes. They called the express team, and I could see them coming in and all the doctors and nurses and all the confusion.
Then all of a sudden I was back in my body, looking up at the
doctor. . . .

A: Can you remember any of the details of what was going on in
the room?

S: They were punching my chest, putting IVs in me, they were
all rushing around there. Everybody was doing something. I do
remember them putting an IV into my right hand and pushing on my chest. Some of the others were packing my belongings because they were going to take me up to ICU. . . . I just
remember seeing everything very clearly, what they were
doing. . . .

A: Were you looking on the backs of the ones standing there?

S: I could see their faces and the backs of the ones who had their
backs to me. In other words, there was a space between me
and my body where I could see what was going on around the
bed. . . .

A: When you got back to your body, were you then looking up?

S: Well, then I could see the fronts of all the people there because
I was in my bed, and they were around my bed. But before, I
was seeing the backs of the people who were on the left of the
bed and the faces of the people on the right hand side of the
bed. . . . I could watch the expression on their faces. I could see
the little needle they were putting in my hand. Something
about the blood gases. . . .

A: Do you recall any other details?

S: Well, I remember I couldn't feel them when they were probing
to put the needle in. That was unusual because you can usually

feel that. I also didn't feel anything when they were pushing on my chest. All I saw was them doing it, but I just didn't feel a thing. I didn't hurt. I could see my face very clearly, and they were lifting my eyelids. They were pulling my eyelids up to look to see where my eyes were, I guess. That's the only way I can explain it. Then they were feeling around my neck where the pulse is. Most of the time it was just this pushing on the chest. I heard the doctor say to get this—whatever the IV was—and this gal was putting this needle in me. . . .

A: Did you see any of the equipment in the room?

S: Yes. They had the breathing machine and a cart with a whole bunch of stuff on it, but I don't know what all those things were. They had the other cart with the IV stuff on it. . . . I could see around the backs of these people, and I saw this one girl grabbing everything because the doctor had said, "We're going to have to get her up to ICU." She was grabbing everything out of my drawer and dumping it in bags and suitcases. When I came to, everything was labeled with my name on it, to go upstairs. . . . [She was never transferred to ICU, however.]

A: Did they use anything off that cart while you were watching it?

S: No. Not that I know of. But the breathing thing they put on my face. It was just a cone-shaped thing that went over my nose. When the doctor was pushing on my chest, they had this on me. They didn't leave it on very long but took it off. I guess they thought it was useless.

A: Did they do any other things to your arms and legs?

S: No. They were more concentrated on my chest, my neck and my eyes.

In summary, this woman claimed to have observed the following events during her autoscopic NDE: the "express team" entering the room with a resuscitation cart; a doctor pushing on her chest; an oxygen mask being placed over her face; an attendant checking her carotid pulse for evidence of heartbeat and lifting her eyelids to check pupillary response; someone starting an IV in her right hand; someone drawing arterial blood gases from an artery in her "hand"; and a nurse gathering up and labeling her personal belongings in preparation for a move to the intensive care unit.

Comment: This woman's medical record, which she had not seen, indicated that she had complained to a nurse at 7:00 A.M. of feeling weak and dizzy. At 7:10, the nurse recorded the woman's pulse to be "weak and thready," her respirations "shallow" and her blood pressure "unobtainable." A cardiac arrest code was called at approximately 7:15 A.M. and a medical intern promptly arrived. At 7:20, the woman was noted to be "unarousable" and an intravenous line was started. A large intravenous injection of concentrated glucose was given in case the reason for her coma was low blood sugar. No response. Additional nurses and doctors arrived on the scene and full resuscitative measures were begun. Arterial blood gases were drawn and sent to the laboratory at 7:30 A.M. Between 7:30 and 8:00, her blood pressure rose to 98/60 and at 8:00 she was noted to be fully awake and complaining of a "slight aching pain across her anterior chest cage." An electrocardiogram showed "no abnormalities." An internal medicine consult was obtained, and it was postulated that a transient cardiac irregularity, triggered by the painful back condition in this diabetic woman with known heart disease, could have caused this episode.

From the medical description in the chart, it is clear that this woman was considered unconscious and gravely ill by those in attendance. Her own account of the measures taken to revive her corresponded with the events recorded in the medical chart. In particular, the procedure used to draw arterial blood from her "hand" was specifically mentioned in her medical record. The remainder of her description focused on the procedural format of the resuscitation, which, like that of Case 1, was extremely realistic from a medical point of view: the starting of an IV, external cardiac massage, the administration of oxygen by mask, the checking of carotid pulsations and pupillary response, and the gathering up and labeling of personal effects.

CASE 3

Mr. J (I–63–2), interviewed in January 1979, was a 46-year-old laborer from a small town in northern Georgia. During his second heart attack and cardiac arrest in January 1978, he encountered the following autoscopic NDE:

> S: I thought I was getting sick, and they had the sides up on the bed. I asked them to pull that can over there so I could heave in it. They wouldn't. I remember I got up on the side of the bed and heaved and that's the last I remember until I was floating right up on the ceiling. I was laying in the bed with the sides up, and the doctor was here and my wife was here

and there was somebody here, I don't know whether it was a corpsman or what. The nurse was on this side of the bed with that machine. She picked up them shocker things and put one there and one right there [pointing to appropriate places on chest] and I seen my body flop like that and I was back. It seemed like it just took me and slammed me right together, you know. It seemed like I was apart and then like two forces coming together in a crash. It seemed like I was up here [pointing to ceiling] and it grabbed me and my body and forced it back, pushed it back.

A: How did it feel when you were up?

S: That was nice. I felt bad because my wife was crying and she seemed so helpless and all, you know. But it was nice. It didn't hurt. . . . I could see but I couldn't feel. I couldn't hear, but I could see everything there.

A. Could you see things clearly?

S: Oh, yeah! Just like I'm looking at you. Real clearly . . . It was just like I could float anywhere I wanted to. I could float through the wall or whatever I wanted to do.

A: Did you try doing that?

S: No. I just tried to get back.

A: You wanted to get back to your body?

S: Yeah.

A: Why?

S: 'Cause of my wife standing there crying . . .

A: How many times did she [the nurse] do that to your chest?

S: Just once is all I know of.

A: You saw that happen to you?

S: I saw it when she put it on me.

A: In clear detail?

S: Yeah. Everybody moved back. I was laying there and when she picked them up and she rubbed something here and here and done something to the end of them. I don't know what she done to them.

A: End of what?

S: Those two little ol' things that you have. Seemed like she wiped them off or done something to them.

A: What do you mean? How did she do that?

S: Well, I don't know whether she touched them together or what.

A: Just kind of show me how it looked.

S: Well, she reached over and got them off the machine like this and either wiped them off or touched them together like that and everybody moved back away from it. First she put this one here [on chest] and then she touched me here and that's about it.

A: How did she make the machine work? Did you see that?

S: There was a switch on it. Them things were there on top and there was a switch down on the right-hand side. I've never seen one of these machines before, believe me. And it seems like she turned the switch on or she picked them up and touched them together and then turned the switch on and then she laid one on my chest right there and touched the other right there. And that's all I remember then.

A: Did you see your body when they shocked it?

S: Yeah. It jumped about that high [gestured about one foot].

A: How soon after that did your experience end?

S: Just like that [snap of a finger]. I never seen her take them off of me.

A: But you saw your body come up?

S: It seemed like I come about that far off the bed and just flopped like a rag doll. . . .

A: Had you ever seen that before happen to anyone?

S: Yeah. I seen it on TV like *Medical Center* or something like that. But I flopped higher than they did [on TV]. It just jars you like that on TV. It seemed like *I* bounced this high off the bed, you know.

A: You said before she put those things on your chest, people backed up?

S: They moved back away from her.

A: Why do you think they did that?

S: I don't know, unless it's an electric charge or something or she told them to. I couldn't hear what they were saying or nothing.

A: Had you ever seen people backing up like that before?

S: No. The only time I've seen that machine used is like when you see a movie and it shows where they put it on the chest—it just shows a little scene of it. It don't show the whole body. I don't even know how the machine works, to tell you the truth.

A: Was there anything else you could see in the room from the ceiling?

S: I knew how the room was set up. You come in the room here and there was a sink and the bed was here and there was a machine here and another machine here, some kind of breathing apparatus, I believe. Could have been oxygen. And they had a cabinet over the top of the sink with some kind of supplies and all in it. I could see that—sheets or something that was white and stacked up. . . .

A: Could you see the tops of their heads?

S: Yeah. Dr. E is pretty thin-headed right up here [on top of head], and I've only seen him about three times. I usually see Dr. F. He's got thin hair here and the guy that was in the room with him was real bald-headed and the nurse had her hair done back like this. She had on a little white cap.

A: And your wife was in the room when this happened?

S: Yeah.

A: What was she doing?

S: Just standing there. Dr. E and this other guy was up by the bed, and my wife was back here. She had just come in the door or something, and she was crying. And then everybody backed up.

A: Did they do anything else to you before they put that thing on your chest and shocked you?

S: They had started an IV in the emergency room already.

A: Could you see through walls?

S: All I was looking at was just me. It just seemed like I was concentrating on just me and what they was doing.

A: Did that seem real to you?

S: . . . I *know* it was real. I know that I was up there. I could swear on a Bible that I was there. But if somebody was really trying to pin me down—can you prove this or that?—there's nothing I can prove. But I know that I was there. I can't prove it to none of those people there because they didn't see me. There's no way you can prove it, but I was there!

A: Was there anything else you could see?

S: No. I really wasn't paying any attention to anything but me and that nurse with those things. It didn't seem important. Nothing seemed important but my wife and that nurse. . . .

A: Did you see things in color?

S: I seen things just like I see them now.

A: Had you ever read or heard of these type experiences before you had your own?

S: No. Because I didn't believe it. I don't believe in ghosts. . . .

In review, then, this man claimed to have "watched" the following events during his cardiac arrest in the intensive care unit of this Georgia hospital: his wife standing near the door, crying; the nurse at his bedside, grabbing the defibrillator paddles and touching them together; people backing up from his bed; the defibrillator paddles being placed on his chest; and his body jolting in response to the defibrillation. No other resuscitative measures were reported. He noticed, however, the general layout of the room as he "observed" it from his perspective near the ceiling and claimed to have looked down on the tops of the heads of others present in the room.

Comment: The doctor recorded in the medical chart that this man was rapidly admitted through the hospital emergency room for a suspected heart attack. An IV was started in the emergency room. Immediately upon arrival in the coronary care unit (CCU), "he developed vomiting, and shortly, ventricular fibrillation [heart stoppage]. This responded promptly to defibrillation."

A monitor strip documenting this man's ventricular fibrillation was included in the "Progress Notes" section of his medical record and indicated that he had already been hooked up to the cardiac monitor in the CCU prior to his arrest. With the immediate availability of a bedside defibrillator in the CCU, the proper treatment of the ventricular fibrillation documented on his monitor was prompt electrical defibrillation. According to the medical records, this was done with success. The man's autoscopic account of his resuscitation also included the description of only one electric shock from the defibrillator, without other CPR measures as described in Cases 1 and 2. Moreover, his description of defibrillation is consistent with routine medical procedure. He "observed" the nurse first picking up the defibrillator paddles and "touching them together." This is a common technique, designed to spread the lubricant evenly over the surface of these paddles to ensure good skin contact on the chest. Next, "everybody moved back"—that is, everyone backed up from the bed to avoid being shocked when the defibrillator was discharged. Then, "she laid one on my chest right there and touched the other right there" and his body "jumped about that high [one foot]."

Since he reported that his wife had been present at the time of his cardiac arrest, I subsequently interviewed her. She recalled having accompanied her husband into the CCU room. She was crying at the time. She saw her husband vomit and fall back in bed unconscious. As the medical team was preparing the defibrillator, she was asked to step out

of the room. She walked around the corner and stood watching the resuscitation through a large glass window which formed the front wall of
the room. Immediately prior to defibrillation, curtains were pulled shut
on this window. When she visited her husband the next day, he told her
about his autoscopic NDE. At first she thought he was "kidding," but
later she became convinced that something strange must have occurred
because, in her own words, "the parts [of the resuscitation] that I saw,
that's what he told me, and all the time this was happening I thought he
was unconscious. I thought if you were unconscious, you really don't
know what's going on."

I later questioned this man again regarding his wife's departure
from his room shortly before the defibrillation. He claimed that he did
not specifically notice her leaving the room, but that this may have occurred, since after the first few moments of the NDE, "All I was looking
at was just me. It just seemed like I was concentrating on just me and
what they was doing." He did distinctly recall seeing his wife crying in
the room at the beginning of his autoscopic NDE, however, which corre-
sponds to the woman's testimony.

CASE 4

Mr. S (I–32), a retired air force pilot from northern Florida, was 44
years old at the time of our interview in May 1978. Five years earlier he
had had a massive heart attack associated with a cardiac arrest and had
had an autoscopic NDE. Our interview follows:

S: I had the arrest the following morning after the night I had my
second heart attack. . . . I think I was sleeping. It was two or
three in the morning. . . . There was no feeling myself that I
was even having an arrest. I wouldn't even have known it unless all the people came around. I think I was probably asleep
when the thing arrested. The first thing I remember is hearing
Code Blue [another term for Code 99] on the intercom and I
remember everyone running in.

A: Did you see people running in?

S: Yes. I think I saw them. I remember faces and the nurses and
Dr. A, who was the internal medicine man at the time, who
happened to be still there.

A: From where were you observing this?

S: I couldn't pinpoint the position. It was almost like I was detached, standing off to the side and watching it all going on,

not being a participant at all but being an uninterested observer. . . .

A: Did you notice anything else in the room besides people? What were they doing?

S: Well, the first thing they did was to put an injection into the IV, the rubber gasket they have there for pushes. I was getting a lot of lidocaine all through that thing, lidocaine pushes, 'cause I had an arrhythmia. Then they lifted me up and moved me onto the plywood. That's when Dr. A began to do the pounding on the chest, and it didn't hurt even though it cracked a rib. I felt no pain.

A: Did they do anything to your face at all?

S: No.

A: Did they breathe for you?

S: They had oxygen on me.

A: How did they administer the oxygen?

S: They had oxygen on me before, one of those little nose tubes, and they took that off and put on a face mask which covers your mouth and nose. It was a type of pressure thing. I remember, instead of the oxygen just being there, it was hissing like under pressure. Seems like someone was holding that thing most of the time.

A: Holding it over your face?

S: Right.

A: Could you describe how that looked?

S: It was sort of a soft plastic mask, light green color.

A: Was it attached to anything?

S: The hose going to the oxygen was all.

A: As far as you could tell, from where you were, would this mask have obstructed your vision if your eyes had been open?

S: Well, the way I was lying, the only way I could have seen would have been straight up, 'cause I was lying on my back.

A: Do you remember any of the other details that went on in the room?

S: I remember them pulling over the cart, the defibrillator, the thing with the paddles on it. I remember they asked for so many watt-seconds or something on the thing, and they gave me a jolt with it.

A: Did you notice any of the details of the machine itself or the cart it was sitting on?

S: I remember it had a meter on the face. I assume it read the voltage, or current, or watt-seconds, or whatever they program the thing for.

A: Did you notice how the meter looked?

S: It was square and had two needles on there, one fixed and one which moved.

A: How did it move?

S: It seemed to come up rather slowly, really. It didn't just pop up like an ammeter or a voltmeter or something registering.

A: And how far up did it go?

S: The first time it went between one-third and one-half scale. And then they did it again, and this time it went up over one-half scale, and the third time it was about three-quarters.

A: What was the relationship between the moving needle and the fixed needle?

S: I think the fixed needle moved each time they punched the thing and somebody was messing with it. And I think they moved the fixed needle and it stayed still while the other one moved up.

A: Did the moving needle ever pass the fixed needle?

S: I don't think so, but I don't specifically remember.

A: What did the rest of the machine look like?

S: It had a bunch of dials on it. It was on wheels with a little railing around the thing, and they had stuff on it. And they had the two paddle affairs with wires attached.

A: What did the paddles look like?

S: Like a round disk with handles on them.

A: How did they operate?

S: They held one in each hand and they put it across my chest, and they seemed like they were squeezing both of them simultaneously.

A: Did you see how they made the machine discharge?

S: With the squeezing or pushing a button on top; I think it was like a handle with little buttons on it.

A: Did you see where they put the paddles on your chest?

S: Right.

A: What did it look like when they discharged the machine?

S: I could see myself jolt, but again, it didn't hurt like an electric shock should hurt.

A: Your whole body?

S: Yes.

A: And this happened how many times?

S: Three.

A: Did they do anything else in the room that you can recall?

S: He was pounding on my chest sort of like a sharp blow.

A: In the sequence of things, where did this occur?

S: He gave the shock first, then he pounded, and then they gave a shock, he pounded again, and they gave another shock and somewhere around that time, I became aware I was becoming conscious and me being me. . . .

A: Did you notice any other details?

S: Dr. A had on his air force uniform, the dark-blue pants with the light-blue shirt, and nurses had on regular whites that they wear. I remember a bunch of people were looking in from what they call the fishbowl. They had a big window between the nursing station and actual ICU itself and there was a little door right around the corner that came into it.

A: You could see through that window?

S: Yes.

A: You noticed people out there?

S: Yes. There were people watching.

A: Were they behind you where you were?

S: They would have been to my left and slightly towards my feet.

A: Did you happen to notice who they were?

S: No, because all the people I knew real well were in the room itself around me. . . .

A: Could you hear what they were saying?

S: Yes. The first thing was the monitor and there was a continuous noise. I heard them calling out watt-seconds on the defibrillator—watts or watt-seconds.

A: Was this scary?

S: No, not really. I was just detached. I wasn't scared, wasn't hurting, just like I wasn't there, but then I was watching it all. . . . Here again, it seems like I was more or less just detached, looking at the thing from somewhere else, a completely uninterested bystander. Unemotional, not hurting, almost like it wasn't me, like I was watching somebody else going through it. . . .

A: Did you know who you were watching at the time?

S: Yes. I knew it was me, but I wasn't concerned about it, for some reason, but yet I knew something serious was going on, but yet it didn't bother me. Like "Look what they are doing. Very interesting!"

A: What's the next thing you remember after you got back?

S: Back conscious?

A: Yes.

S: I remember there were still all those people around and they were checking pulses, looking at the monitor, blood pressure.

A: Were you looking up from where you were then?

S: Yes. Looking up from my back.

A: So there was a definite difference from where you were looking up and from where you were observing this before?

S: Yes. Definitely. I couldn't pinpoint a position where I had been, but it was almost like I was in an amphitheater, and I was observing it. I was at the foot of the bed or to either side. . . .

A: Did you feel like you could go anywhere else when you were in this detached position?

S: I could have walked around or whatever. I was free to do whatever I wanted, move around, watch what was going on. . . .

A: Had you seen a resuscitation before?

S: No. I never had.

S: Had you watched it on a TV program?

S: I don't recall ever having seen it on TV.

A: Had you ever watched or seen this defibrillator work before?

S: Never.

In short, this man claimed to have viewed the following events during his autoscopic NDE: doctors and nurses rushing into his CCU room; an injection into his IV line; the cardiac board being placed behind his back; movement of the dials on the face of the defibrillator while it was being charged; the pressing of "buttons" on top of the defibrillator paddles to discharge the defibrillator; the jolt of his body from each of three separate defibrillations; external cardiac massage between defibrillation attempts; and the holding of a light-green oxygen mask, which was "hissing" under "pressure," over his face during the procedure.

Comment: This man's medical record indicated that he had had a cardiac arrest in the CCU during the early-morning hours of his second hospital day. He was successfully defibrillated. Other specifics of the CPR procedure were not available.

From a general medical standpoint, this man's autoscopic report of his resuscitation accurately describes what would be expected during a CPR procedure performed by highly trained personnel in an intensive care unit setting. I was particularly fascinated by his description of a "fixed" needle and a "moving" needle on the face of the defibrillator as it was being charged with electricity. The movement of these two needles is not something he could have observed unless he had actually seen this instrument in use. These two needles are individually used (1) to prese-lect the amount of electricity to be delivered to the patient ("they moved the fixed needle and it stayed still") and (2) to indicate that the defibril-lator is being charged to the preselected amount ("[the moving needle] seemed to come up rather slowly really. It didn't just pop up like an ammeter or a voltmeter or something registering"). This charging proce-dure is only performed immediately prior to defibrillation, since once charged, this machine poses a serious electrical hazard unless it is cor-rectly discharged in a very specific manner. Moveover, the meters of the type described by this man are not found on more recent defibrillator models, but were in common use in 1973, at the time of his cardiac arrest.

Had this man, from his training as an air force pilot, been exposed to CPR instruments and techniques which would have enabled him to give such an accurate, detailed account of his own resuscitation without having actually observed it from his autoscopic NDE? Throughout the interview, he used various medical terms ("lidocaine pushes," "defibril-lator," "watt-seconds," etc.) which might suggest that he possessed a rather sophisticated knowledge of medical jargon and procedures. When asked about this, he explained that he had paid close attention to what was being said during his autoscopic NDE and could recall much of the words and conversation used by the doctors and nurses present ("I heard them calling out watt-seconds on the defibrillator—watts or watt-sec-onds"). Moveover, he flatly denied having ever seen this CPR procedure, including the movement of the needles on the defibrillator, at any other time. The tone of this interview and of subsequent conversations I have had with this man have convinced me that he would have no reason to lie about these statements. I feel this way partly because of his consistent downplaying of the significance of his own experience throughout our conversations. While he was quite sure that he had watched his own resuscitation as if "detached, standing off to the side" and that the things he had observed were real, he nevertheless was not impressed with the occurrence itself. He was one of the few persons I interviewed who was not convinced that his NDE represented anything unusual:

It's like a dream. You're detached from the thing and watching it as a bystander. . . . Really the only explanation I can have is that the brain still functions even though it is partially dead, or starved from oxygen. Everybody believes you are out cold, but you are still perceiving things even when you can't talk or move . . . visually and audibly [perceiving things]. . . . That's it. That's the way it is. It hasn't changed my thinking about life, death, the hereafter or anything else. It's one of the facts of life you can't explain.

In the two and a half years following our initial interview, this man has consistently maintained the same attitude toward his NDE in the talks we have had together.

CASE 5

Mr. M (I–67) was a 62-year-old retired mechanic living in a small town in northern Florida when I first interviewed him in March 1979. A year before, he had suffered a heart attack with a cardiac arrest, during which he encountered the following autoscopic NDE:

S: When they got me to the hospital they took me in there and done pulled my clothes off me and put me upon the table. That's when I really had the heart attack. . . . Then all of a sudden it seemed like I moved up. I got up. The room seemed like it was in a glow. I don't know where the light was coming from. I was looking down and they were working on me. Just like getting up out of the bed, just about. I was above myself looking down. They was working on me trying to bring me back. 'Cause I didn't realize at first that it was my body. I didn't think I was dead. It was an unusual feeling. I could see them working on me and then I realized it was me they were working on. I felt no pain whatsoever and it was a most peaceful feeling. Death is nothing to be afraid of. I didn't feel nothing. They gave me a shot in the groin. Dr. B came up and decided to put one in my left—well, not in my armpit, but on my side. Then he changed his mind and went to the other side, next to the heart. . . . I seen them trying to bring me back with those pads. They put something on those pads like a lubricant, it looked like, and rubbed them together and put them on my body, and then it jumped. But I couldn't feel it, even at that time. They brought it back and then hit it again when it went right back out again. . . . [Later] When Dr. B seen me, he told me I had a close call and died and all that stuff. I told him, "Dr. B, I couldn't have died. I knew everything that went on." I told him when he came up under my right armpit and changed his mind and went to the other side. He said it was impossible and that I couldn't have possibly seen that, and that I was legally dead at that time. He just shook his head. He just couldn't understand it. And I asked, "Am I right?" He said, "Yes, you're right!" He just shook his head and went walking off. . . . I felt like I was alive. It was just as though I was standing there talking to you. I could hear them and see them working on me and hear them talking and giving them orders and directions. It seemed like I was above my body and seeing everything that was going on. . . .

A: Were you still awake when they first brought you into the emergency room?

S: Yes, sir.

A: Did you lose consciousness somewhere along there?

S: No, sir. I never lost consciousness, except the only time I went out was when they seemed to move back from me. They got off at a distance. I never blacked out. He [Dr. B] said I had to have blacked out, but I never really blacked out. It was just like I got up and moved.

A: How high up were you when you were looking down?

S: Just above their heads. I could see them well. . . .

A: How were they working on you?

S: They put those pads on my chest. He was calling out certain numbers or something or other. The only thing I could figure was that they were putting an electric shock to my body or something like that. I knew my body was jumping every time they put those pads on me.

A: Had you ever seen that before?

S: No, sir.

A: Did that hurt?

S: No, sir. I had no feeling. I didn't even feel those shocks they put in.

A: Did you see your face at the time?

S: Well, not directly. I saw it a couple of times, but they were in the way. There was a nurse standing at my head and the doctor was standing at the side with those round-like pads in his hands.

A: The first thing they did was put the pads on your chest?

S: No. They gave me those shots first in the groin down there somewhere. It appeared to me they were putting a shot in there. My right side.

A: Could you see a cardiac monitor?

S: Yes, sir. It was to the right of the foot of the bed. I could see it at first when it was jumping and then it quit. After the first time they tried to bring me back it jumped a few times and then it quit again. That's all I could see.

A: How many times did they shoot the electricity to you?

S: About five or six times they tried that thing. I could be wrong, but about five or six times.

A: Each time they did this, was it done the same way?

S: Just about. It seemed like they moved the pads around on my chest a little bit. When I come to in the intensive care, now, I had burned marks all over my chest.

A: Did you see how they worked the machine?

S: No, sir. He was calling out some kind of numbers to them, and she was over there operating it, and he had it in his hands.

A: What did those things on your chest look like?

S: They looked sort of like round metal pads and about one-quarter or one-half inch thick.

A: Could you tell me about how they were trying to stick a needle in your armpits?

S: It looked like he started to come in under the right armpit and then he changed and come in on the left side. He didn't put it directly under the armpit but between my breast and armpit. It looked like a needle to me.

A: Did he draw some blood out of it?

S: No, sir. I believe this was a shot. Some kind of a shot.

A: Did he start an IV in it, or do you know?

S: You mean a line?

A: Yes.

S: No, sir. Not that I know of.

A: Did you happen to notice anything else in the room?

S: They had my clothes there, and they moved them up and put them between my legs at first. Then they moved them later.

A: Did they push down on your chest any?

S: I believe Dr. B was a few times, but otherwise he was using those pads.

A: At what point did you come back down?

S: The second time around when he used those pads. I call them pads. He rubbed some kind of lubrication on them. That's when they brought me back, and that's when I came back to my body.

A: Was it after one of those times he shocked you?

S: Yes. Next thing I remember, I was back in the body just like it was before. I was kind of sore.

A: This was a different vantage point than before?

S: Yes, sir. No question about it.

A: When you were looking down, could you see the tops of people's heads?

S: Yes. Most of them had their heads covered up. There were two nurses standing at my head, two at my foot, and some standing there working that machine. I don't know what you call it—an electrocardiogram or whatever it was. Whatever they used to shock me with, I presume. I believe there was about five or six in there altogether.

A: Now, you said Dr. B told you that what you saw really happened?

S: Yes, sir. And Dr. B must have told Dr. G about it, because Dr. G came in later and told me that sometimes your mind hasn't had time to die and you can still see things. But I told him that it appeared that I was above my body looking down instead of down there with my body.

A: What do you think this was that happened to you?

S: Dr. Sabom, I think it's God's work. That's the only thing I can figure. God had me that time and he could have kept me. From this experience, I know there is a life after death and not just death itself.

A: Have you told many people about this?

S: Just a few, because some people will think you're crazy. But I know what I saw, and I know the experience that I had. I'd heard of it but I'd never believed it.

Comment: This man's medical record was as follows:

This 60-year-old Caucasian male was brought to the emergency room by ambulance at 4:25 P.M. On his arrival, he was alert, anxious and complaining of chest pain. On physical exam, he was slightly cyanotic but his cardiopulmonary exam was otherwise normal. At 4:50 P.M. he was given ¼ grain of morphine sulfate and an electrocardiogram was obtained and was normal. Shortly thereafter, he went into atrial fibrillation with straight line [on cardiac monitor] and then ventricular fibrillation [heart stoppage]. Full cardiopulmonary resuscitation was instituted. The patient was cardioverted to normal sinus rhythm with occasional premature ventricular contractions [skipped heartbeats]. Arterial blood gases were drawn during the procedure and sent to the laboratory. Electrocardiogram at 5:15 P.M. showed sinus tachycardia. Intravenous atropine was given at 5:15 P.M., one ampule of sodium bicarbonate at 5:16 P.M., and ¼ grain morphine sulfate at 5:25 P.M. Patient was admitted to the intensive care unit with a diagnosis of cardiac arrest and probable acute myocardial infarction [heart attack]. Because of persistent hypotension [low blood pressure] following the arrest, a dopamine drip was begun to maintain his blood pressure at a systolic of 100 millimeters of mercury.

The man's own account of his resuscitation as he had "observed" it during his autoscopic NDE included a description of the cardiac defibrillation. He had noticed that a "lubricant" had been applied to the surface of the two "pads" before they were placed on his chest. The procedure he is describing here is quite common and involves the application of a gel-like substance onto the surface of the defibrillator "paddles" to ensure good skin contact at the time of defibrillation. The paddles are often "rubbed" together to spread the gel evenly over their surface.

The man described "a shot in the groin" during the resuscitation procedure. According to his medical records, arterial blood was drawn from his left femoral artery during CPR to measure the amount of oxygen in his blood. This procedure is accomplished by inserting a small needle and syringe into the groin area to obtain the blood. If observed from a distance, it could easily be mistaken as the administration of a "shot." A discrepancy arises here, however, since the man claims that this "shot" was given in his right groin, whereas the arterial blood gas laboratory slip identifies the site of puncture as "LF"—left femoral. It is of no medical significance which side of the body the blood was obtained from, which raises the possibility that the lab slip is in error. On the other hand, the man may have been suffering from a right-left confusion as he related his account. If he had looked down on his body from the foot of his bed, the right side of his physical body might well have been on his left in relation to his point of observation. Just such a right-left confusion was evident in another portion of the interview, when he describes the doctor inserting a needle initially on the left side of his chest and then changing his mind and inserting it on the "other side, next to the heart" (the heart is on the left side). He later corrected this error: "[the doctor] came up under my right armpit and changed his mind and went to the other side."

Finally, this man's description of additional "shots," "[not] directly under the armpit but between my breast and armpit," is a portrayal of attempts by his doctor to enter the subclavian vein, which is located on both sides of the chest under the collarbone. This is a frequently used procedure to gain access to the central venous system for the administration of drugs during a cardiac arrest or to insert pressure-monitoring catheters or cardiac pacemakers. From his medical record, we know that this man's blood pressure was quite low following his resuscitation and that it had to be maintained with intravenous medication (dopamine). It is quite possible that his doctor was attempting to insert a catheter to monitor cardiac pressures at the time of these "shots"—an appropriate step to take if a patient is on medication to maintain his blood pressure. Many times it is difficult to find the subclavian vein, deep in the chest, during the rushed circumstances of a cardiac arrest, and the usual procedure here is to attempt it first on one side, then on the other. If my reasoning is correct, this is exactly what happened, based on the man's "observations." This "failed procedure" was not mentioned in the medical summary since its mention would have served no useful purpose. This *is* the procedure, however, whose occurrence this man's physician supposedly confirmed to him at a later time. Fortunately, the outcome of the CPR and the man's eventual recovery were not dependent on the successful completion of this procedure. His intravenous medications were apparently administered through a more peripheral IV line (probably in the arm) which was already in place at the time of his cardiac arrest, since the records show that he had received a quarter-grain morphine sulfate "IV push" at 4:50 P.M.

I later interviewed this man's wife. She and her daughter first learned of his NDE the day after the cardiac arrest, when he told them of the details he had observed during his resuscitation, emphasizing the calm and peaceful nature of the experience. Furthermore, this woman said that her husband rarely retells his experience, but when he does, it has always been consistent with his original description.

Finally, I talked briefly with the man's physician. Although he could not recall the details of this particular resuscitation (it had occurred over two years previously), he did say that he had had several patients over the years who had told him of these types of experience and that this man's case could well have been one of them.

CASE 6

Mr. O (I–57) was a 60-year-old retired laborer when I first interviewed him in August 1977. In July 1976, he had suffered a heart attack associated with a cardiac arrest and a combined NDE. The autoscopic portion of this combined NDE was described as follows:

S: I went into the third heart attack and it was a real bugger. They said I was going into all kinds of spasms. . . . As I was going, I could see my body lying there as I looked back with no remorse. . . . I saw the whole show, and I didn't know who it was at first, and then I looked real close and it was me and I thought: Oh, man, what is this? And I didn't feel no different than I do now. I was looking from up, down . . . I was going up slowly, like floating in a dark or semidark corridor like. They were working the hell out of me. They were crawling on top of me with their knees. Actually, they cracked my pelvic bone on the right side and that's right where I saw that knee as I was going up. . . . They were all shaking their heads as I was going up, but I didn't see them do that . . . [use] these electric jobbies to hit you with. . . . They were all done with that, I guess. I didn't feel rejected or any remorse or nothing. . . . And I saw them stick the needle in there almost in the center of the chest but on the left side. . . . They just plunged it in and gave me whatever that fluid was. . . . I could see things very clear, very vivid. . . . They put that needle in me and nothing happened so they started crawling all over me again, beating on my chest, pushing on my chest, banging with their fist on my chest. I had three fractured ribs on the left side. . . . And I kept thinking: What is this? What's happening? And I kept going up and up and up. . . . I couldn't hear anything. Not one peep. I was doing all the evaluating in my mind. . . . And I remember seeing them down the hall just as plain as could be. The three of them were standing there—my wife, my oldest son and my oldest daughter and the doctor. . . . There was no way, being out, that I could have seen anybody. . . . I knew damn well they were there. . . . I didn't know what was going on. I didn't know why they were

crying. . . . And then I went further. . . . I went to a different
world. . . .

A: Were you unconscious while this happened?

S: Oh, yes.

In other words, this man claimed to have viewed the following
events during the autoscopic portion of his NDE: an injection into the
heart; external cardiac massage; and the presence of his wife, eldest son
and daughter standing down the hall of the hospital.

Comment: The portion of this man's medical record that described
the details of his cardiac arrest could not be located. His autoscopic recollection of the resuscitation included mention of an intracardiac injection and of external cardiac massage. The most interesting aspect of his
testimony, however, was his maintaining that he had seen three family
members standing "down the hall just as plain as could be" and that
"There was no way, being out, that I could have [physically] seen anybody. . . ."

I separately interviewed this man's wife regarding his account. According to her, her husband had been on the ambulatory floor of the
hospital that night, anticipating hospital discharge the next day. She had
planned not to visit him that night since he would be coming home so
soon. Quite unexpectedly, her eldest son and daughter came by to visit
her at home and the three of them decided to surprise him with a visit,
"since we didn't have anything better to do." Without phoning ahead,
they arrived at the hospital and began walking down the hall that led to
his room. They noticed "a lot of commotion" in the hallway adjacent to
his room and a nurse stopped them, "at least ten rooms down," from
going any farther. The woman recognized her husband's gray hair and
knew something was wrong. He had just been wheeled in his bed out of
his small double room and several doctors and nurses were working on
him. His face was pointed away from her, and all she could see was the
top of his head. He was then taken directly up to the intensive care unit
on another floor without passing by his wife and children. The next
morning, when they were allowed to see him, she found him to be disori-
ented and unable to talk because of "the tubes in his mouth and nose."
Three days later, his condition improved and he was able to describe to
her what had happened. In her words:

He seen everything. He seen them working with him. And he told
me he seen us standing down at the end of the hall. And he couldn't
have seen us because his head was facing us [the face pointed the

other way]. He couldn't have seen us. . . . He swore he'd seen us, and I said he couldn't have. And even if he had just been laying there in the hall without the heart attack or anything he couldn't have recognized us from the distance. . . . And what was funny was that I wasn't always with the same people. We have six children, and they're all grown. So when we went down to see him, it was never the same. One time one daughter would go or another daughter or son would go or me. So he couldn't have known who I was with or that I was even there. And he told me who was there. . . . He said he seen us standing there talking to the doctor. And we were. . . . And when he told me the different things that he had seen, it's always the same. He never changes it.

I also interviewed this man's daughter who had been in the hospital that night. Although she could not recall many of the exact details of this particular visit (her father had been hospitalized several times that same year for heart attacks and she had difficulty keeping his admissions straight), she did remember arriving at the hospital with her mother and brother at the time of her father's cardiac arrest. She could recall this since it was an unexpected event on the night prior to his anticipated discharge from the hospital.

Conclusions

In comparing the details reported in these six autoscopic NDEs with the events of the actual crisis and routine medical procedure we have seen that these persons have given credible portrayals of their ordeals. While their assertion that they observed these details from a location removed from their physical bodies should be assessed, other, more traditional explanations for this phenomenon must first be ruled out.

1. *Accurate portrayal of the near-death crisis event based solely on prior general knowledge.* Earlier in this chapter, I mentioned the possibility that a person's general knowledge of CPR technique prior to his own cardiac resuscitation may enable him "blindly" to reconstruct the events following his cardiac arrest without having actually "observed" them from an autoscopic location. Twenty-five "control" cardiac patients were then interviewed to evaluate their level of knowledge concerning CPR technique. None claimed to have had an autoscopic NDE during a cardiac arrest, but their backgrounds were similar to those who did. Eighty percent of these control patients committed at least one major error while attempting to describe in-hospital CPR from their own per-

sonal knowledge of this technique—a rate of inaccuracy not seen in descriptions of CPR based on an autoscopic NDE. This suggests that the CPR descriptions from an autoscopic NDE were not based solely on the person's prior general knowledge of CPR.

The proposal that the autoscopic NDE is based on one's prior general knowledge of CPR technique is cast further in doubt when the type of CPR details reported from the NDE is evaluated. These autoscopic details appear to be fairly specific for the actual resuscitation being described and are not interchangeable with the clinical circumstances of other near-death crisis events. For example, the man in Case 3 said his CPR consisted solely of cardiac defibrillation—a description that fit with the actual events as reconstructed from his medical record. The man in Case 5 described the performance of several additional procedures, including a "shot in the groin," a description consistent with *his* medical situation, but inappropriate for the condition of the patient in Case 3. Nor would the autoscopic description in Case 3 have fit with the medical situation in Case 5. This suggests that the autoscopic description of CPR technique is relatively specific for the resuscitation being described. If this autoscopic description had been based on "prior general knowledge" of CPR technique, this specificity of details for the resuscitation in question would not have been found.

2. *Accurate portrayal of the near-death crisis event based on information supplied by informed observer.* It is always possible that the accuracy of the autoscopic NDE could be attributed to information passed on to the near-death survivor by someone (a doctor, a nurse, etc.) who witnessed the resuscitation. I find this possibility unlikely for two reasons. First, the type of information contained in the autoscopic descriptions is not what would likely be explained to a patient recovering from a cardiac arrest. It is usually appropriate to explain to resuscitated patients that their "heart stopped beating" and that an "electrical shock" was used on the chest to stabilize cardiac rhythm, but there is no conceivable reason to supply the details reported in the typical autoscopic NDE—the insertion of a plastic airway, the checking for a carotid pulse or pupillary response in the eye, the drawing of arterial blood from the hand or the groin, the movement of the needles on the face of the defibrillator, etc. Second, several patients claimed that they reported the autoscopic experience soon after the resuscitation. Interviews with family members confirmed these claims. Moreover, these family members had observed that the original description of the NDE was consistent with subsequent retellings of the experience by their resuscitated relative.

3. *Accurate portrayal of the near-death crisis event based on visual and verbal perceptions made during a semiconscious state.* Much like the surgical patient who can sometimes hear conversations between physicians and nurses in the operating room while under general anesthesia (see preceding chapter), the unconscious near-death patient may also hear verbal remarks made during his own resuscitation. If these are later recalled by the near-death survivor, then perhaps his autoscopic NDE could be explained as the piecing together of verbal information into an accurate *visual* image of what actually transpired. In the foregoing six cases, however, several of the autoscopically perceived events were of a nonauditory nature (e.g., the pattern of movement of the needles on the face of the defibrillator). Moreover, the interpretations of some of the autoscopic details indicate that the perception of the detail was *visual,* not auditory. For example, the man in Case 5 described "a shot in the groin . . . It appeared to me they were putting a shot in there. . . . " The procedure he is describing is not an injection, but the drawing of blood from the femoral artery for a blood gas determination. If his autoscopic description of this procedure had been based on remarks made by others present, then he would not have misinterpreted the intent of the procedure. However, such a misinterpretation could easily be understood if the man had watched it from a distance, as he claims; for the "shot in the groin" would then have been a logical conclusion based on the *visual* observation of the insertion of a small needle and syringe into the area of the groin.

But could the autoscopic perceptions have resulted from intermittent visual glances of the resuscitation through the physical eyes of a semiconscious individual? Again, I find this unlikely, since many of the details described in the autoscopic NDE were of objects and events outside the visual field of the person being resuscitated. The most striking example here, of course, was given by the man in Case 6, who identified three of his family members standing in a hospital corridor at a time when his head was pointing in the opposite direction.

Thus we have attempted to explain the apparent accuracy of the autoscopic NDEs by prior general knowledge, by information passed on by another individual, and by physical perceptions of sight and sound during semiconsciousness. None of these possibilities have been found to be plausible explanations.

Some other explanation must be sought to explain these findings—a task to be undertaken in the closing chapters of this book.

8

"Afterexperiences": Recurrent Autoscopic Encounters

THIS HAPPENED back in July 1964. I was on my way to a dental appointment and I was rushing and it had been raining. I was having to catch a bus and I crossed a pedestrian crosswalk but it did not have traffic lights. . . . I was walking across and a man yelled at me and I wheeled around to see what he was saying—apparently he was trying to warn me—and I was struck from behind by a black car. . . . That's the last thing I remember until I was above the whole scene viewing the accident. I was very detached. This was the amazing thing about it to me . . . I don't remember hearing anything. I don't remember anybody saying anything. I was just viewing things. . . . It was just like I floated up there . . . [up to the] rooftop or maybe a little higher . . . very detached. I think the thing that impressed me the most was that I was devoid of emotion. It was as though I was pure intellect. I wasn't frightened. You know, it was very pleasant and obviously emotionally detached from the whole situation. . . . [I remember] seeing my shoe, which was crushed under the car. . . . I remember seeing the earring which was smashed. I remember wearing a new dress and I was wearing it for the second time—at that time I made all my clothes—and I thought: Oh, no. My new dress is ruined. And I wasn't even thinking about my body being possibly ruined too. This is an odd thing in that I don't think really that the seriousness of the situation dawned on me. I don't think I really had the realization at the time that: Oh, my God. I'm outside my body. What's happening to me? . . . The next thing I saw was the woman [the driver of the car], crying. . . . She was standing by the car and the car was stopped right where everything had happened. . . . I remember seeing the car being dented. And I saw my body. My attention was called to my body when the attendants put it on the stretcher. . . . I saw myself in profile. I was actually towards the front and side of the car, viewing all of this. The ambulance was actually in back of the car. I was viewing my body as they picked it up and put it onto the stretcher. It was from a distance away, actually. But I saw myself in profile. . . . I remember them looking at my eyes. I guess they were checking my pupils, I don't know. Then they began lifting my body in that peculiar way. I really got the impression that they were just yanking the body up and getting it to the hospital as fast as they could. The way they handled me was something else. . . . This was amusing to me because they lifted me in a very amateurish way. They just picked me up underneath my shoulders and underneath my knees rather than rolling the stretcher up under me and then lifting me onto whatever they put me into the ambulance with. There were two of them [attendants]. I thought they were supposed to be professionals and they don't know what they're doing. I remember thinking in a very detached way that that certainly wasn't the way to handle an accident victim. The whole thing was very detached. I remember them putting me—that is, putting my body—into the ambulance. After that, I don't remember anything else until I awoke in the emergency room and my mother and my minister were there and I understand they had already done X-rays and things. . . . And the next thing I remember was that I was crying in the emergency room because I couldn't see. . . . I awoke blind and couldn't see for about thirty minutes after I fully regained consciousness.

A: Did you later confirm the fact that you had lost a shoe or an earring?

S: Yes. Those were returned to me. Both were returned to me and of course one earring was broken, but the shoe wasn't really damaged. That's funny; it [the car] had run over the toe of it, or I guess it had. I never got that confirmed. . . . And I remember thinking how odd it was that I was knocked out of my shoes. I didn't learn until much later that this is common and what happens when you get hit.

A: Did you ever talk with the woman who hit you?

S: Yes. She said she was not looking where she was going. She said she had a little boy with her, but I don't remember seeing him through all that. I remember asking her if he had stayed in the car and apparently he had. I don't remember seeing the child. She said she was looking at him at the time of the accident, and I asked her, "You mean he was with you?" And she said, "Yes." And I said, "Did he stay in the car?" And she said, "Yes. He did." Maybe in viewing that thing I was so interested in what was going on with me that I didn't notice him in the car. (I-6)

In the hospital, this woman was told that she had suffered a "nasty concussion" and a "hematoma that was a third again as big as my head." This was an epidural hematoma—one caused by bleeding from a ruptured artery lying, as she put it, "between the lining of the brain and the skull." She was treated with medications and strict bed rest for three weeks and recovered without residual brain damage.

When I interviewed her in November 1979, thirteen years after the accident, she was a 32-year-old saleswoman, living in northern Florida. Her experience appeared to have been a typical autoscopic NDE. Prior to this NDE, she claimed to have had little if any interest in "psychic" literature.

But I became interested in it afterwards because I wondered what was going on. . . . I knew that I had left my body [during the NDE] because this became something I could do almost at will. I realized that I had *learned* to do that at that time and that I had probably come close to dying. . . . It was not something I could talk with people about. I mentioned it to my mother, and she looked at me in a peculiar way as if: "You poor child!" For that reason I didn't talk with anyone else about it.

When asked to explain what she had "learned" at the time of her autoscopic NDE, she told me the following:

After this experience it seems that I was able to leave my body. This would occur at night and I would simply get out of it and see it lying in bed. My husband was working for the forest service and was gone at night, and I would be afraid. But it seems like I could just get out of my body and see it lying there and go check on everything. We were living in a house trailer at the time. The first time it happened, it was just a matter of weeks after my accident. . . . It was a spontaneous thing. I was very concerned because I was hearing noises . . . it was late at night. I don't have any recollection of time. Time seemed irrelevant and that seemed odd because I'm a compulsive clock watcher. . . . I left my body. . . . I just walked back and forth within the trailer looking out the windows and everything to make sure everything was all right and then I went back and got back in [bed]. . . . And I had powers to go to whatever height I wanted and I was not limited, as I am in my physical body. . . . I was very lucid while I was outside of it. . . . I guess I floated, because I don't recall walking. . . . While I was sleeping, I was anxious about leaving the body there, almost as if I resented it for not waking up. . . . It was as if: "You lazy creature, you're just going to lie there and let these things happen to you. Somebody is going to have to look after you." I'm serious now. I know it sounds insane. It really sounds off the wall. I know it does. But that's honestly how I felt. I was angry. You know how you become angry with your body when it becomes ill and it lets you down? It was a similar feeling. . . . I routinely started doing this to check on things. The next time it happened, I realized I was unlimited. . . . I went down the street and came back. . . . It was just a deserted neighborhood at night . . . [but] it scared me to leave the body unattended there [in the trailer]. And I remembered thinking that the body couldn't function without this part of me in it. That it would lie there and sleep . . . [and that someone would] do something to it before I could get back in. That scared me so I didn't leave the trailer anymore. . . . [One time while out of body] I found a door open in back. I mean wide open. The back door in the trailer. I left my body and traveled down to the end of the hall and the back door was standing wide open and we never used that door. We always came in and left by the front door. It was as if I couldn't do anything about it in that [out-of-body] state . . . apparently when I was like this I had no physical capabilities. I had the power of looking and that's it. . . . So I went back and got in my body. Then I got up physically and went back there and it [the door] was open. . . . When I was pregnant about a year later, we moved to an old house and the windows were very high and they locked at the top. You had to get a chair to lock the windows. Well, when I left my body to go see if all the windows were locked—and my husband was there at the time—it had just become such a routine thing with me to make sure everything was all right. And I thought: Gee, this is really neat, when I realized there was really unlimited powers. What caused me to stop doing this was after my son was born. I would routinely go check on him in this state to make sure he was all right and I thought it was very convenient I could do that. I got to thinking that if I happened to get out of it [the body] and for some reason could not get back in, there would be nobody to care for my son. I really thought I had better stop this because I really had not done anything fantastic with it, and it really hadn't served any useful purpose except for a convenience. So I decided not to do it anymore and I didn't. I never tried it since then. . . . [It had gone on for] about two years, dozens and dozens of times. It became commonplace. . . . I became very comfortable with it. . . . I have read a couple of books on astral travel, but because of these people's occult influences, I generally disbelieve what I've read. There was nothing occult about this. I had some of these experiences while awake. I just wanted to make sure I wasn't dreaming. I wondered if I could do it while I was awake and I found that I could. I could get outside my body and still walk down the street. But I stayed right with it [the physical body]. I just jumped out and jumped right back in, just to see if I could do it. And I could and that satisfied me. . . . And that was what was neat about it, because I thought: Well, if I'm not dreaming, then this is either real or I'm insane, because I know now that it is happening. . . .

A: So these differ from dreams?
S: Oh, yeah! They're different. They really are. Most of my dreams, to be quite frank with you, are in the third person. That is, in my dreams, I'm seeing myself play a role. If I am in the dream, I am the observer. But when I was in that [out-of-body] state, I was actually "physically" present—I was really carrying out those things. I was in the first person, detached from my physical body. The "I am" was there [out of body] and the physical body was just a shell. . . . And I have never had any drugs and have never even smoked a cigarette. I was just a good little Baptist girl.

According to this woman's testimony, then, she began to have "out-of-body" experiences similar to her autoscopic NDE following her automobile-pedestrian accident in 1964. She could voluntarily "separate" from her physical body, usually while sleeping at night, to carry out some purposeful action, such as checking on the condition of her infant son in the next room or ensuring that her windows and doors were locked for the night. These experiences were quite real to her. Occasionally, discovering something unexpected while "out of body," she would return to her physical body and then *physically* go to verify her "out-of-body" visualizations—such as the open back door in her trailer. The thought of "leaving" her sleeping physical body concerned her, however, since she felt that it could be harmed without her actual "presence" dwelling within. She eventually "gave up" these "out-of-body" experiences because of her fear that she would be hurt during an "excursion," and unable to care for her son.

Two other persons in this NDE study claimed to have had similar types of afterexperiences following an NDE during a true near-death crisis event. The 33-year-old triple amputee who had had an autoscopic NDE during a battlefield explosion in 1969 described his later experiences as follows:

This happened after my trip to Vietnam. It's happened three times. All three circumstances are identical and I think that has a lot to do with it. It normally happens after I have been up for three or four days in a row. I get very tired and lay down for a brief nap. All three times I'm just laying in bed at home and I just come up out of my body. Again, I'm always up in the upper left, looking down at my body, and I know it's me. The three times that I've done it I've done three different things The first time I did it, I floated up and down Interstate 20, which is the interstate where I live. Why, I don't know. . . . When I was going up and down Interstate 20, I could see cars and people. It was almost like I could get right beside the window at sixty or seventy miles per hour and not move. I would look into the car like I was riding right beside them. And then I would just float on off to another car. It was almost like I was looking for someone or somebody, but I never found it. I had no perception of length of time. It's very, very real. . . . The second time I did it was very funny, but it got verified. Next door to me is a nurse, a very good friend of mine for about ten years. I've always kidded her about the fact that one of these days I'm going to take a shower with her. Now, that was kidding. The second time I came out of this thing, I went over through the buildings and into her shower, where she was taking a shower. Two days later she said she felt me in the shower with her. I said, "Wishful thinking on your part!" I was kidding her about it. The third time I did it, I didn't leave my place at all but just floated in my room. And then, all of a sudden, I came right back into my body. I don't know how to explain that. It's not filtering. It's not going through the head. It's just that I'm not there anymore but I'm in the body again. I don't have any explanation for it. If I told people that, they really would think I'm crazy. I'm in complete control of my faculties, but I don't have any explanation for what this is. . . . It was very, very clear. Like I'm looking at you.

A: Are these similar to your experience on the battlefield?

S: No. There's no bright light. There's no communication on my part [with deceased comrades]. It's just a relaxed atmosphere. It's still a terrific feeling. . . . The apartness from the physical body seems to be the same. I definitely felt like I was separated.

A: Did you feel like you had died during these three experiences you have had since your return from Vietnam?

S: No. I could see me breathing. I knew that I was there. But I always wake up realizing that I had done it. I wish I could control that, because it's a good, peaceful feeling. But it doesn't happen every time I'm really that tired. Only three times in the past ten years.

A: Are these different from a dream?

S: Yes. Because I was out of my body and I saw me laying there. Whereas when I dream, I see through here [indicating eyes]. When I dream, I see out through my body. When I have these experiences, it was with this, whatever this was, I was seeing it through that. . . . Moreover, dreams are not always real. Having left the body was very real. Dreams are sometimes fantasies. Most of them are things we would like to see happen or have happened and we just redo them. (I–68)

The third person to describe afterexperiences was a 55-year-old dress designer from Florida who had had a combined NDE during an episode of hemorrhagic shock following a tonsillectomy. Several years later, the following episode occurred:

Now, I have never heard of this before, and I have never told anyone else. You're the first one I'm telling this to. I was in church one

Sunday evening and the lights were on and our church was a very old one and the ceilings were extremely high, with balconies in the back. I was listening to the sermon, and I left myself on that seat. I don't know how or why—I never could understand it. I was all the way up to the top of the ceiling and when I did, it was the most difficult thing I had to do to get myself back down in that seat. I must have gone up in a spirit or something. I don't know. But anyway, I did. All the way up to the top of that ceiling . . . all I could see was that church and I felt myself just raising on up. . . . I was already up to the top of the ceiling and I thought: What am I doing up here? It frightened me. . . . Now, what in the world would have happened if I had kept on going I don't know. Whether the ceiling would have opened up and I would have gone on through, I don't know. (I-41)

Because only three cases of afterexperiences were found in the over-all study, their relationship, if any, to the original NDE is unclear. All of them first appeared *after* the true NDE, however, suggesting that this "ability" was somehow facilitated by it. In fact, the first woman mentioned in this chapter felt that her ability to go "out of body" had been "learned" from her autoscopic NDE during the auto accident. Could some latent human ability have been activated by the near-death crisis event, allowing these autoscopic experiences to repeat themselves under non-near-death circumstances? This question will be addressed in the final chapter of the book, where the autoscopic NDE, autoscopic "afterexperiences," and other types of autoscopic experiences will be further considered.

9

Implications of the Near-Death Experience

LITTLE HAS BEEN SAID of the implications these NDEs have for tne lives of those who have encountered them or for the medical community which is charged with the care of these individuals during their near-death crisis event. Throughout this study, I have had the opportunity to consider these implications from the standpoint of both the near-death survivor *and* the medical institution. What I have observed convinces me that the NDE is a truly significant event for both the patient and his physician. Moreover, the psychological impact of this experience at the point of near-death may play a role in the physical outcome of the resuscitation itself by affecting a powerful but poorly understood aspect of human life—the "will to live."

Implications for the Individual

By far the most important implications of the NDE lie with the individual who has encountered the experience. Almost every subject interviewed in this study indicated, in his own way, that his NDE had been a truly remarkable and important event in his life. Some even described it as the "peak" event, which had done more to shape the depth and direction of life goals and attitudes than any previous single experience. The impact of the NDE on these persons was evident in many different and unique ways.

Most commonly, death anxiety was dramatically reduced, if not totally eliminated, by the experience. Individuals surviving similar types of near-death crisis events *without* associated NDEs, however, did not evidence this change in death fears (see Table XIV). Furthermore, this reduction in death anxiety was readily evident not only at the time of the initial interview but also months or years later (see Table XV). Associated with this decrease in death anxiety was the strong personal conviction that the NDE represented a privileged glimpse of what was to occur at the moment of final bodily death.

This reduction in the fear of dying was apparent in the life of a 43-year-old New Jersey man following an open-heart operation, postoperative cardiac arrest and NDE:

A: Has this [NDE] had any effect on you?

S: Yeah. . . . I'm not afraid to die anymore. . . . Still, even today, I'm not afraid to die anymore and I feel this [NDE] has a lot to do with it.

A: How does it have anything to do with it?

S: I just feel that when I die, I'll be with them [deceased relatives encountered during NDE]. (I–44)

This man's mother later told me that when her son first spoke of his NDE, she had dismissed it as a hallucination associated with his critical medical condition. Months afterward, she began to question her original impression of his experience—which remained "just as clear in his mind now as it was when he first told me." Moreover, the NDE had had a definite effect on his attitude toward dying. Before the experience, he had said many times, "I don't want to die, I'm too young to die"; after it, he said, "Well, I'm going to do the best I can, and when my time comes, I'm ready for it."

His death came three years after his open-heart surgery and postoperative NDE. Shortly thereafter, his widow recalled her husband's account of his NDE, while he was recovering from the surgery—the bright white light he had seen, along with the visions of deceased relatives and friends urging him to "go back," for it was not his time to "be there." According to her, he had carried this experience with him until his death and had kept insisting on how real it had seemed. Moreover, he never deviated from his original description of it. She had known him to be "not the type of person who would have read about those sorts of things." As his death approached, she had been amazed at how he appeared "prepared to go" and how he even "prepared us [his family] for his death." Thus his NDE seemed to him, to his mother and to his wife to have been a major turning point in his ability to deal with the prospects of dying young.

When new attitudes regarding death and the "hereafter" were integrated into the lives of individuals such as the man above, a new fervor for day-to-day living was often apparent. For the terminally ill or dying, the effect was usually to focus attention on living for the "here and now" and away from a preoccupation with death and fear of the unknown. The NDE did not, however, cause these individuals to deny the reality of approaching physical death or wish for its hastened arrival. To the contrary, an intuitive acceptance of both life and death appeared to emerge. This resulted in a renewed "will to live" instead of an accelerated "will to die." Such was the case with one of my cardiac patients, who had a transcendental NDE during a cardiac arrest from a massive heart attack shortly after his thirty-third birthday. I have followed this man closely as an outpatient since his crisis event and have come to know him and his family quite well. Medically, he has inoperable cardiac disease, is severely disabled and unable to work. Since our first meeting, however, I have been continually impressed with his degree of adjustment in going from an active and fulfilling personal and professional life to an extremely limited existence which has markedly altered his life style. During one of many conversations we have had over the past two years, he told me the following:

> S: It [the NDE] just changed my whole life like a flipflop. . . . I used to worry about life and living it and trying to get ahead, trying to make life easier by working harder to make more money to make life easier. I don't do that no more. . . . I just live from day to day. I used to live for what was ahead or behind me. You can't live a day in advance or a day behind. You can only live for the day that you're living. . . . I know that I don't have as much life as other people might have. I know that already. But I'm going to live what I've got left and I'm going to enjoy it. I know where I'm headed to, so that I don't have to worry about dying anymore. . . . I've been through death and it don't bother me. I'm not scared of it. Death is nothing to go through anymore. It's not that hard to

die. . . . I know where I'm headed to and I've got my life to
live. I enjoy it a lot more.

A: Do you think it would have been different if you had just had a
cardiac arrest and not had that experience?

S: I think so, because if I'd just had a cardiac arrest I'd've been
just like everybody else, I wouldn't have experienced death like
I did. I know that it's real to myself. It actually happened to
me. (I–15)

Though this man no longer feared death, he regretted parting from
his family, and his remarks during this portion of the interview evidenced much emotion:

S: I put a lot of burden on her [his wife] a lot of times. She's
picked up a lot of responsibility. She's head of the household
now. When she took me back into the hospital this past spring,
she thought I was dead again, because I was paralyzed from
blood clots. I just couldn't move. I could hear her scream. It
was a scary scream. She walked into the room where I was at
and saw what was happening to me and I couldn't breathe.
She thought I was gone then. It's put a burden on her because
she doesn't know when I'm going to go and everything that
happens to me is just part of her, I guess. She feels like she's
going with me or something. That's how close it's drew us. I
don't want her to be that close to me, because I know it's going
to hurt her just that much more when it does happen. She's
accepted it, but it's still going to break her down quite a bit
when it does happen because she's gone through so much that
when I go, it's going to be like a part of her, I imagine. The
children, they've gone the same way. When I come up here the
other day—my boy and I are close; he's fourteen; we're close
but he's got a mind of teen-agers—he came to me and I was
sitting in the pickup when we started out. He said, "I want
you back home," just like that, and turned around and walked
off. [Pause] Things like that hurt you when they're walking
away from you, somebody you care about. It's hard to accept.
[Pause] That's life.

A: You seem to have gone through a lot and done well with it.

S: Yeah. When you go through life, you live a life. Lot of people
who have children and they die before they die, they pick up
automatically and they know what I'm experiencing. It's hard

to accept some things, but some things you've got to accept. I've accepted my life as being short. It's going to be a short life and my family has gotten pretty well close to it.

The NDE was also helpful during the acute and painful stages of recovery from the near-death crisis. The following case is of particular interest in this regard because of the numerous painful and near-fatal events endured by this man during a protracted hospitalization for kidney failure and multiple associated complications. Throughout his ordeal, he claims to have been sustained, in part, by the memory of the NDE he encountered while en route to the hospital. In his own words:

> When the doctor put me in the ambulance to take me to Gainesville, my wife told me later that he told the ambulance driver that I probably wouldn't make it. I had already had about five convulsions already. I was in a state of semiconsciousness. . . . I was hurting real bad . . . tremendous pain. Later, for four or five weeks, I was in real bad shape. I had a cerebral hemorrhage. I was in a coma for seven or eight days and I had all those other convulsions. . . . When I had the cerebral hemorrhage, they gave me up and took all the medicine away; had tubes in my nose and everywhere, took everything away, and Dr. H told my wife that there was no way I could live through it. No kidney patient at that time had had a cerebral hemorrhage and lived. . . . They had a terrible time getting the peritonitis cleared up. They gave me up on that. They told my wife I wouldn't live through the night. Then my blood pressure went up to about 250/190 and I had the cerebral hemorrhage. They said that even if I did live, I would have no mind. After about seven days I came out of it. There were about three days where I had trouble remembering things like having been a fireman, what kind of car I had, where I lived and things like that. . . . It's [the NDE] done a lot for me. . . . I know that death is not all that bad that you should worry about it, so it doesn't bother me. . . . Now it doesn't bother me at all. So it's really helped me a lot through all this I've gone through. I'm really not worried and I think it's sort of helped me maintain my sanity through all this. (I-53)

This new attitude toward death also affected the person's views upon the death of loved ones. The process of grieving was often reported to have been made easier by the "knowledge" that the recently deceased had passed on into a painless and peaceful existence. The potency of this personal belief was usually attributed to the previously encountered

NDE. The woman whose testimony is excerpted below had suffered a severe episode of toxemia of pregnancy, which resulted in unconsciousness associated with an NDE. One year later, her husband unexpectedly died. Her reaction to his death was influenced by attitudes that had developed since her NDE.

> My husband died shortly after this [the NDE] and he was given the last rites. Usually I would have been hysterical, but I was calm because I knew that his pain and everything was over and that he was happy. That's the advice I give to anyone dying—not to cry or scream. My husband passed away in 1956 and my mother-in-law said that it must have been when I delivered [and encountered an NDE] that I became so calm when my husband passed away. I don't cry when anyone passes away. I know that their pain is gone. (I–48s)

Another man—the Vietnam veteran who encountered an NDE during a battlefield explosion in which he lost both legs and an arm—expressed similar views about the process of mourning another's death:

> [Following the NDE] I don't go to funerals. I don't send flowers. I don't tell people I'm sorry. Somebody tells me somebody died and I say we should be happy. Why don't we have parties at death? In my will I will have no funeral or tombstone. I will be burnt, with my ashes dispersed. I think it's a waste of time and a waste of land and it's something we should be partying about. They left for a better life, a good feeling. I don't think I'm screwed up by thinking that. My family does. I think that I'm way ahead of everybody else. I'm not afraid to die. I firmly believe everything happens for a purpose. . . . I live, play and work as intense as I do because I realize the very next instant I could be gone and I might not come back into the body that time. . . . There is something after life. It is a good feeling. [During the NDE] I think I was at total peace with myself. I didn't want to come back. It was different. It was not void of life or feeling, because it was a beautiful feeling, and it was a life. Whatever life it was, whatever form we were in, we existed. (I–68)

The religious views of persons encountering an NDE were commonly strengthened by the experience itself.* This strengthening of previous beliefs was usually evidenced by a marked increase in formal

---

* However, no change in the basic type of religious belief occurred—that is, no agnostic became a believer, no Protestant a Catholic, no Catholic a Jew.

religious activity or personal commitment. One man put it this way:

> I believed in Jesus Christ before [the NDE] but I didn't actually
> live it. I live it today. The biggest reason I think I'm here today is
> that I haven't lived a full life and Jesus Christ gave me my life back
> to finish living it. . . . I know when I die I'm going right back
> through the same thing [the NDE] again. . . . When I was in that
> tunnel [during the NDE] and came out, I knew my life was given to
> Jesus Christ. . . . Now, don't get me wrong. I guess I'd been like
> everybody else and tried all the adventures in life while I was in the
> service. I drank. I had a business and had to drink and associate
> with people in order to keep a business going. In today's world, you
> have to socialize with business in order to keep a business on its
> feet. You have to do everything you can to keep your business going.
> I found out later that you don't have to socialize with them to keep
> your business going. You can tell them you're a Christian and that
> you don't care for their drinking and they'll accept it and go on. (I–
> 15)

Another man was a volunteer at the hospital where I was working.
While treating him one night in the emergency room for a painful bout
of gastritis, I noticed from his medical chart that he had previously suffered a heart attack and cardiac arrest. When I questioned him, he denied any recollection from the period of unconsciousness. About an hour
later, he cautiously approached me and privately described a vivid transcendental NDE which he had been embarrassed to talk about. He then
explained how this experience had affected his religious beliefs and why
he was now a hospital volunteer:

> A: What do you think this episode (the NDE] was?
> S: I couldn't really say, but I think that's when Christ came into
>   my life. . . . It completely changed everything as far as my way
>   of living. Before that I drank beer and whiskey and a lot of
>   things I wouldn't do now. . . . I couldn't wait until I got out of
>   the hospital [after the NDE] to go to church. The pastor said
>   he had never seen anyone so anxious to come forward and ac-
>   cept Christ as I was.
> A: Before your experience, did you attend church?
> S: No. I never went to church.
> A: Has this affected other aspects of your life?
> S: Well, I promised the good Lord that I was going to work for

him the rest of my life and that's what I have been doing. I work for the Veterans Volunteer Service, where I can go around and visit patients and talk with them and hand them things that you can hand them out. It seems it opens the door for me. I can talk with them a little bit. I have two tape recorders going in the hospital right now.

A: What are those tapes of?

S: Church programs. I tape one every Sunday morning and Sunday night at church. The church gives me the tapes. (I–25)

The religious beliefs of another man were deepened by his NDE in the following way:

S: It's brought me closer to the Lord, also, and the Bible. And I try to go along with both of them and those guidelines. . . . I used to go out and get wild and get drunk. But not anymore. . . . I was not only hurting me but my wife and kids. I realized that from these experiences [NDEs]. I care more than I did. I care more for my family, and it's brought my family closer.

A: Do you think that's a result of those experiences or a result of you being sick?

S: I think it was those experiences, because my being sick really didn't bother me. I figured that from the time you're born you're destined to die and that's all you live for until your destination. *Now* I believe there's a lot more to live for than to just reach your final destination. (I–62)

A vivid transcendental NDE enriched the religious faith of yet another man, who now confessed that he was 100 percent committed to the Lord:

This [experience] has taken a lot of the load off me. But I still have struggles in living the faith, but I realize the grace of God takes care of all that. But in my life I have discounted a lot of trivial things I used to worry about. The Lord has allowed me through this experience to separate what is important from what is not important. That has been a terrific boon to me. . . . He made me through this experience to be able to completely put myself in the hands of the Lord and totally believe. . . . You can imagine what a boon that is to my life to be able to totally commit myself 100 percent without any reservation. . . . Most men have trouble with their pride. This has ceased to be a problem, to a great extent anyway. At least it doesn't trouble me, because I understand the Lord's grace. Also, I was born into a farm family with very, very modest circumstances, and I've always had a great desire to be real prosperous. Well, I don't think anybody would mind being prosperous, but I see how little it really does mean to my faith. I found out that some of these things are really laughable as far as importance. So all I need now, in my way of thinking, is to be able to survive comfortably, and since I've turned myself over to the Lord completely, he has blessed me with a message I couldn't have foreseen otherwise. And I truly believe that he has controlled all of this for my benefit. (I–65)

Following the NDE, vocational choices were often made which allowed the person's newly acquired attitudes and beliefs to be incorporated into his daily activities. One woman who became a hospital volunteer said that other hospital personnel became aware of her calm acceptance of death and often called upon her in the following way:

Later [after the NDE] I went to work in the hospital as a volunteer. One of the girls who was a psychologist and social worker kind of knew how I felt about things and a lot of times they would call her if a doctor had to tell someone that he was going to die because they would like to have someone around afterwards. When she heard of someone who was upset, she would always call me and have me go in to talk to the people because if they were going to die, it didn't bother me. It was really easy for me to talk to the people about it. I'd feel really good about it, and it seemed to make the people feel better. (I–70s)

A new personal interest in the caring and loving aspects of human relationships often developed following an NDE. This change was directly attributed to insights gained from the NDE itself. From a hospital social worker: "I think what it [the NDE] has done is make me more sensitive towards people." (I–37) Another woman put it this way: "When I look at people now, I feel that I really do love them, which is something I never felt before." (I–40s) Expressed in yet another way: "I feel that we are measured a great deal by what we do for others. That we're all put here to help one another . . . the greatest law we have is love." (I–52)

At the conclusion of several interviews, I asked whether or not the person who had encountered the NDE felt that his experience carried with it a "message" for other people. The following were typical responses:

> If people would accept death and [that] it's not a frightening experience, that it's going to happen and they're going to have to experience it one day, then they would live their life a lot easier. (I–15)

> I'd be quick to say to you that I don't worry about it [death] because when the time comes there will be a total sense of peace pervade all of your thinking and it will be a very restful feeling. (I–55s)

> That's the advice I give to anyone dying, not to cry or scream. . . . I don't cry when anyone passes away. I know that their pain is gone. (I–50s)

Thus we find that the NDE has powerful implications for the daily lives of many individuals during the acute stages of recovery from the near-death crisis event, during the more prolonged stages of a terminal medical illness, and/or during a return to health and to normal living.

Implications for Our Medical Care System

Given the importance of the NDE to many survivors of a near-death crisis, how should this information affect the attitudes and practices of physicians and other professionals charged with the care of sick and dying patients? First, the nature and existence of the NDE demands professional recognition. In my experience, such recognition is not yet widespread. For example, in the fall of 1977, two years after the publication of *Life After Life,* I distributed a brief questionnaire to the audience of a Psychiatric Grand Rounds on Near Death Experiences at the University of Florida. Ninety-five questionnaires were returned by fifty-eight paramedical personnel, twenty-one physicians and sixteen nurses. Nearly all had worked closely with sick or dying patients. Only ten of these respondents, however, were aware that an NDE had occurred in one of their own patients (43 percent of near-death survivors from this same hospital population were found to recall an NDE when interviewed). Following this presentation, however, nearly all of those present felt that an awareness of these experiences would be professionally helpful in dealing with certain patients in future clinical situations.

In my own experience, I have often been appalled at careless conversation by physicians and others at the bedside of a comatose or cardiac-arrested patient as they editorialize on the grim details, the hopelessness, of the situation at hand. Many patients deemed unconscious and otherwise unaware of ongoing proceedings during a near-death crisis event can often "see," hear and later recall details of what transpired in the vicinity of their physical bodies (see Chapter 7). From what we now know, it is imperative that these "unconscious" patients be treated with all the care and respect that would be afforded a conscious, alert individual.

In addition, the occurrence of these phenomena should not be interpreted as an overt manifestation of an abnormal psychiatric process. In a traditional medical textbook, I found a rare mention of the NDE:

> Most commonly, it is impossible for a patient to clearly remember the events surrounding cardiac arrest followed by successful resuscitation. A vivid account is provided, however, by a 68 year old patient who experienced a cardiac arrest in a Canadian hospital (MacMillan and Brown). He was being monitored for a possible myocardial infarction when a ventricular premature beat fell on a T wave, provoking ventricular fibrillation [cardiac arrest]. The patient was defibrillated and subsequently recovered. To him, the experience was extremely vivid. He remembers looking at his watch and noting the time. Suddenly he was aware of giving a very deep sigh and that his head "flopped" over to the right. At this point, he apparently lost consciousness. The patient then describes himself as leaving his body and he was able to observe it "face to face." He had a feeling of floating in space and of considerable tranquility, and he remembers thinking "so this is what happens when you die." He recalls that after traveling at great speed in space, there was a sudden sensation, almost of a sledgehammer variety, in his left side. Having received six such shocks, he opened his eyes. . . . After the experience was over he remarked to his doctor that the floating part of his sensation was so strangely beautiful that "if I go out again, don't bring me back—it's so beautiful out there."[1]

Aside from this brief account, no further comment was made regarding the causes or implications of this NDE. The medical reader was left with the impression, however, that such an occurrence had clear psychiatric implications, since the material was included in the "Psychiatric Complications" section of the chapter devoted to "Complications to other organs and systems in cardiac resuscitation." Further, it was sandwiched between paragraphs dealing with "severe personality decomposition," "acute brain syndrome," and "other psychiatric reactions" to the stress of medical care in hospital intensive care facilities. However, the NDE has not been shown to be an abnormal "psychiatric reaction" (see Chapter 10), but seems to be occurring in a sizable number of sane, stable individuals who are unconscious and physically near death. To continue to assume the hallucinatory or psychiatric (and, by implication, abnormal) character of the NDE will merely perpetuate the feeling of isolation that many of these individuals have experienced when they attempted to discuss their encounters with physicians or others in attendance.

For example, shortly after being resuscitated from a cardiac arrest, one woman attempted to discuss her NDE with the doctors and nurses present. She had observed the resuscitation during an autoscopic type of experience and was curious as to its meaning.

A: Did you mention this [NDE] to anyone there?

S: Yes. To several doctors and nurses who were there, but they just sort of scoffed at me. You know how they do . . . and I said, "I don't believe what just happened to me." Of course they wanted to know what and I told them and they looked at me and sort of scoffed and that was it. . . . They just said it was the pain that caused it and that I couldn't have seen all this.

A: Did it seem real at the time?

S: Yes, quite real.

A: What do you believe this was?

S: Well, I really don't know. I've been rather puzzled about it. (I–45)

Moreover, many of these people confessed that they would have greatly appreciated an opportunity to discuss this event with others in an atmosphere of openness and understanding. As it was, private contemplation of this matter often caused them to question their sanity. After a particularly vivid transcendental NDE during a cardiac arrest, one man put it this way:

A: Did this [NDE] seem real to you at the time?

S: You better believe it. So much so that afterwards it preyed on my mind. I did not, right away, say anything to my family, but as I started getting better and was taken out of intensive care and put in a private room in the hospital, there was a Catholic priest right across the hall from me as a patient. I did open up and discuss it with him. I thought I was cracking up or something and he said, "Not at all," because he had heard of cases like this. (I–61)

Still another cardiac arrest victim, after encountering a combined autoscopic-transcendental NDE, questioned his mental stability after the experience but felt unable to discuss these concerns with others, for fear of ridicule:

A: Had you ever read or heard of people having similar things to what you experienced?

S: No. That's why it's kinky for me. That's why it scares me, because I don't like to think that I'm that unique. But I must be unique in that sense. . . . There are some other aspects of this which are real hairy and sometimes I think that I'm going mad. . . .

A: Have you told a lot of people about your experience?

S: No, sir. You're the only person.

A: Why?

S: People will think I'm crazy. I wouldn't dare tell my wife. She would have me a candidate for the second floor [psychiatric ward]. But you've expressed an interest in it and you seem sincere. I'm not telling you everything, Doctor. Just enough so that you won't get too uptight with me. Maybe later, when I know you better and know how serious you really are about this thing. It's a pretty kinky experience. (I–19)

Psychiatric referral was actually initiated in the case of one woman, who had told her parents and physician of her NDE during a severe auto accident that occurred many years before, while she was a teen-ager:

I told the doctor that something had happened to me. I said, "There was this light and this voice spoke to me. Do you think that was God?" I was fourteen years old, and he said, "No, I don't," and he told my parents. My parents pondered it for a long time. Then they asked me about it, and I told them without any fanfare or anything that this is what I heard and this is what I saw. . . . I was never afraid! At first they thought I was in shock and then they realized that I wasn't in shock and that I was all right. I was never afraid. They questioned whether or not what I was saying was true. They were questioning me, and then they said, "O.K." Then two months later we were going downtown or something and they said we were going to stop in and visit this doctor and I said, "O.K.," thinking it was for them. Then there was this psychiatrist and I said, "You've got to be kidding. . . ." The first one I told about the experience was the doctor, and he immediately had my parents send me to a psychiatrist. . . . The psychiatrist said to my parents that this was just a result of the accident and me wanting to say something had happened. They convinced me of that. I felt that I had done something wrong by saying what had happened. I don't feel that way now, yet it [peace] didn't come until years later. I feel it was God, and it was a very religious experience for me. I am a Christian. . . . With that, I am 37 years old, and I have never told anybody about it since.*

Another implication of the NDE for our medical care system is one I have observed in my own practice over the past few years—the effect on the doctor-patient relationship. Recently, the medical profession has been widely criticized for its alleged preoccupation with the technical aspects of medical care and a concomitant diminished emphasis on close patient rapport. This criticism has quite frequently come from terminally ill or dying patients, precisely the individuals who represent "technological failures" and are most in need of a supportive physician relationship. These individuals are also likely to have encountered an NDE during the course of their illness.

Given these needs of many sick or dying patients, I have found the following helpful in my own practice. When I began this study, my primary goal was to validate the existence of the NDE. As the interviewing progressed, however, I began to realize that these conversations served a much greater purpose than the academic collection of interesting facts and data. For the individuals who had had an NDE, the sessions appeared to fulfill a need. Most of these people had been unable, for one reason or another, to discuss this aspect of their medical illness, which they had felt to be of great personal significance. Many had wondered whether they were "cracking up" and were relieved to find through our conversation that other sane and normal individuals had encountered similar experiences while unconscious and near death.

One patient of mine with a chronic heart condition had had a cardiac arrest and an NDE in 1976. After telling me of his NDE, he described how upset he had been at his inability to discuss his experience with the doctors and nurses who were caring for him ("I was afraid they would have thought something was wrong; that I was making it up or goofy or something"). His post-resuscitation anxiety was clearly documented in the progress notes section of his medical record by his doctors and nurses:

First hospital day: (Description of cardiac arrest and resuscitation)
Second hospital day (A.M.): "noted to be extremely anxious"

---

* An interview number was not assigned and the content of the NDE was not included in the overall study since this woman was not sure whether she ever lost consciousness during the accident, which resulted in the death of several others in her car.

Second hospital day (P.M.):   "still nervous and apprehensive—also questions constantly. . . . Patient remarked that 'I have delusions like I'm here but I'm like four feet away from my pain.'"*

Seventh hospital day: "continuing to be a nervous wreck"

Twelfth hospital day: Patient signed out of hospital "against medical advice."

Demerol, a narcotic painkiller, had been given to this man prior to his cardiac arrest on the night of admission. He continued to receive shots of Demerol for chest pain throughout his hospitalization, despite his fear that it would induce another cardiac arrest. This fear was well documented in his chart. During my interview with this man four years later, he told me that the "delusion" he had during his cardiac arrest had worried him even more than the Demerol injections. Moreover, this "delusion" had been, in essence, an autoscopic NDE, which he described to me in the following way: "I was sort of in a floating position. . . . I seen my face. It was about four feet below me and I could see it. . . . I recognized me laying there." His thoughts during this NDE had caused him to feel considerable guilt at the time:

> I could have moved away from my body anytime I wanted to, but that made me feel guilty. I wanted to go [die], but I had a wife and a couple of children. I wanted to leave there real bad. All I would have had to have done was to have thought it, and I would have been there. I knew that, see, and it made me feel guilty for a long time. About a year or so, I guess. It just seemed like a terrible thing to think. It made me feel guilty that I was willing to put my welfare ahead of someone else's. I wanted to leave real bad. I don't feel guilty about it now. I've just come to believe that that's just the way things are. There was a choice. (I-5)

At least part of this man's post-resuscitation anxiety could have been avoided if he had been able to discuss his NDE openly with the doctors and nurses without feeling that "they would have thought something was wrong . . . [that he was] goofy or something."

This need to discuss his NDE with the medical staff was expressed by another patient of mine following a heart catheterization at the University of Florida in 1978. During the procedure, he had suffered a brief

---

* Despite the suggestion in the nurse's notes that this man had had more than one "delusion," he states that this occurred only once, at the time of the arrest.

cardiac arrest, from which he was quickly resuscitated. Later that same day, I was talking with him about the catheterization findings. He expressed concern over his cardiac arrest and over some "feelings" he had had while "unconscious." (He was completely unaware of my interest in NDEs at this time, and my purposes at that moment were *not* to interview him for this study.) I asked him to elaborate on these "feelings," and he hesitantly began to describe an autoscopic NDE. He had apparently "watched" from the corner of the room as we resuscitated his body. We discussed his experience in detail. His concluding remarks: "I'm really glad you told me others have had these experiences. I was really worried about that!" (I-30)

Simple reassurance that the NDE is a common occurrence among sane and "normal" individuals during a near-death crisis event was also quite helpful to a woman who had had a transcendental experience during a surgical operation. Prior to our discussion, she had "tried to analyze the whole thing, but couldn't figure it out" (I-40s). She had been unable to discuss her NDE with her doctor for fear of being judged "unstable." Despite the pleasant nature of the experience itself, she had had several nightmares about it ("I was trying to get the answer [to the meaning of the NDE] in my mind, but I couldn't"). She then read a newspaper account of a lecture I had given on NDEs at a local medical school. She contacted me, and we arranged a meeting. At the end of our conversation, she expressed great relief at having been able to discuss her experience and at discovering that others had had similar encounters.

All these cases illustrate the great need many patients have to discuss their NDE, in an atmosphere of openness and understanding, with physicians and nurses in attendance. Moreover, calm reassurance that the experience is not the initial manifestation of a psychiatric illness is certainly beneficial. If such an interchange can occur between patient and physician, then the doctor-patient relationship will likely be elevated to new levels of trust and acceptance. Accordingly, I am continuing to question all my patients who have survived a near-death crisis event about a possible NDE, not only to gain further insight into the experience but to strengthen my professional relationship with the patient.

A more direct, open communication between the near-death patient and his physician regarding the patient's experience and feelings during his period of critical illness may also afford the physician the opportunity for growth in relation to his *own* attitudes regarding death. In this regard, several studies have suggested that physicians' attitudes toward death may be in need of some reform. To wit: the views of two prominent psychiatrists on this matter:

What makes one death appropriate and another death tragic? It is strange that while medicine presides daily over unnumbered deaths and psychiatrists study the psychopathology of death in its protean forms, death has so universally been regarded as a dark symbol beyond investigation. Psychiatrists do not hesitate to study various types of suicide, but the reverse of a suicidal situation, one in which the prospect of appropriate resolution in death far outweighs the fear of dissolution by dying, is rarely mentioned. Part of the answer to this is to be found in the aversion among doctors to confront themselves with the fact of their own death and to wonder if death can ever be appropriate for them. Despair wears many masks; a hard shell of materialism may cover a tenderness that shuns exposure. The dedication to forestall death is an indication that the medical profession believes that death is never appropriate.[2]

While this statement may sound extreme, other studies have found that many physicians do indeed have difficulty in handling personal death fears and anxieties. This, in turn, may interfere with physicians' ability to communicate honestly with terminally ill patients. One such study, entitled "Physicians Consider Death," evaluated these feelings among 81 physicians (internists, psychiatrists and surgeons) and compared them to age-matched control groups of both healthy and seriously ill individuals. The findings, in part, concluded that:

The physicians also displayed significantly (.05 level) more negative verbal death imagery than the (seriously ill) patients and blocked in this area reliably (.05 level) more often than the normal population. . . . The notion of personal death was also rejected more vigorously by the physicians than either the patients or healthy subjects. Reaction of the physicians to the death of another person was revealing. "Feel bad" and "Sorry" were responses from the physically ill and healthy, whereas "Would make me reflect on my own mortality" was a competitively conspicuous reaction from physicians. Interestingly, although the overwhelming majority of physicians wanted to be informed if they had an incurable disease, they were less willing (.01 level) than the patients to provide such information to others in the same boat.[3]

These findings are supported by a similar study, entitled "Attitude of Psychiatrists Toward Terminally Ill Patients": Here, 100 percent of the psychiatrists polled said they wanted to know of their illness, 93 percent of them at the time of diagnosis. Yet when asked if they would tell their patients of terminal illness, only 54 percent said they would always tell them and 34 percent said they would tell them only occasionally.[4]

Moreover, these difficulties in honest doctor-patient communication may be evidenced at the bedside of the terminally ill patient.

As one patient so eloquently put it:

I'll be damned if I share my feelings about death and dying with anyone
who makes 2-minute U-turns at the foot of my bed.[5]

These observations describing the present inadequacies of our medical care system in communicating with and handling the problems of
terminally ill patients have been underscored through my participation
in a group known as CITE (Cancer Isn't The End), sponsored by a
local chapter of the American Cancer Society. The purpose of this group
is to bring cancer patients and their families together to discuss problems
they are facing in living with cancer. By far the most frequently discussed difficulty is the failed communication between cancer patient and
physician. From the moment the diagnosis of cancer is made, these individuals have expressed a need for medical information and support—a
need that they feel goes largely unmet and that intensifies as their disease progresses.

Symptomatic of these unmet needs expressed by cancer patients and
their families is the widespread and growing use of unproven, nonmedical cancer remedies. Such is the case with Laetrile—an extract derived
from apricot pits. Legal activity has recently become intense to legalize
(and, by implication, legitimize) the use of this unproven therapy for the
treatment of cancer. As noted recently in the *New England Journal of
Medicine:* "All of this activity is in the face of continued strong opposi-
tion from vitually every reputable cancer specialist and major medical
organization in the country." This article then asks:

> What are the options at this point? One approach is to legalize Laetrile
> for general use now with the requirement that it later be evaluated retro-
> spectively. . . . [A second approach includes] a prospective controlled clini-
> cal trial dismissing the objections of some that such a course would be
> unethical. . . . [Finally] a retrospective review of existing clinical case rec-
> ords, to determine whether there is any documented evidence of an objec-
> tive beneficial effect.[6]

But are the results of just "one more study" really going to have the
needed impact to change the minds of thousands of cancer victims who
have turned their backs on the opinions of "virtually every reputable
cancer specialist and major medical organization in the country"? Or is
some additional problem being grossly overlooked, as is suggested by
these follow-up comments by two concerned physicians?

> . . . what is behind the American public favoring the legalization of Lae-
> trile is a protest of medicine's lack of understanding of the real issue here.
> . . . It will only be after Medicine addresses itself to man's fear of disabil-
> ity and death that Laetrile will disappear. Next year, it may be a different

form of quackery, such as coffee enemas, but as long as it is offered with concern, respect and a thread of hope it will persist. *Gentlemen, stop wasting your money on further study; listen and respond to the screams of your patients as they grapple with their fear of death.* [Italics mine][7]

The message seems clear to me. People with cancer, and the American people in general, are saying to the medical profession, "You are not meeting our needs." If we persist in ignoring this message, and continue to concentrate obsessively on trying to prove the inefficacy of Laetrile, patients will simply find another Laetrile and yet another.[8]

At the institutional level, this medical attitude toward death and dying is also in need of review, since death continues to be traditionally viewed as a frightening and merciless enemy. Such is the portrayal of death as found on the wall of one of our chief hospitals (see page 143). Here, in full view of hospital patients and staff, the strength and technology of modern medicine is depicted in mortal combat with a grotesque, skeleton-like figure of death (the "grim reaper"). Given the positive effects of medical research to improve and to prolong the useful lives of many individuals, is it really necessary or appropriate to envision death in such a negative context? Is this image what we wish to convey to our terminally ill patients, many of whom regularly pass by this symbol? This "message" has, after all, the tacit support of the medical institution.

Another reflection of medicine's institutional attitude toward death and dying is the lack of emphasis placed on this subject in medical training. In the 1977 article "Attitude of Psychiatrists Toward Terminally Ill Patients," it was found that 73 percent of psychiatrists interviewed felt that the best way to learn when and how to tell a patient about his terminal illness was through clinical and formal teaching. In addition, 93 percent "indicated that the subject of 'terminal illness, death and dying' should be included at both the graduate and undergraduate levels of medical training." Unfortunately, as of May 1978:

the medical Establishment is still slow to accept the health care reforms prescribed by the death-awareness movement. In the American Medical School, death is often regarded as a personal failure, an affront to a physician's power or a threat to his rescue fantasies. One recent survey of 107 U.S. medical schools, prepared by the Foundation of Thanatology at Columbia Presbyterian Medical Center, showed that only seven had a full-time course on thanatology.[9]

Thus we find that the pervasive attitude of our medical care system

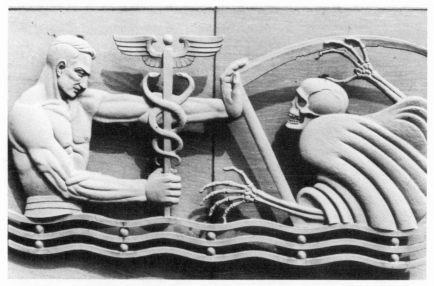

Emblem of "death" found on the wall of a building that adjoins the entrance to one of our leading medical institutions.

toward death is not meeting many of the needs of dying patients and may be creating unnecessary fears and anxieties in many other patients. These attitudes toward death have not been formulated from the results of serious scientific research into the clinical aspects of death and dying. Rather, they have emerged from a lack of such research. Granted that the mysteries of death are not readily amenable to controlled laboratory investigation. Nevertheless, our best available evidence for what dying is actually like—the attitudes and experiences of those who have come closest to actual physical death—has been largely ignored by our medical and scientific communities. When examined in a "scientific" fashion, however, the great majority of these near-death survivors who can recall specific events during the unconscious, near-death period describe these events as calm and peaceful—quite unlike a meeting with the "grim reaper." Should not these "data" be considered more seriously in shaping and directing the attitudes and goals of our medical care system as it attempts to meet the needs of sick and dying patients?

Implications Within the Field of Death and Dying

In 1969, *On Death and Dying*[10] appeared as an eloquent statement of the needs and concerns of the dying patient in our society. Written by an American-trained psychiatrist, Dr. Elisabeth Kübler-Ross, this book spurred a new interest in the problems of the terminally ill. The field of "death and dying" came into its own. The following are among the goals of this newly established field: (1) to challenge conventional cultural avoidance and denial patterns of death; (2) to find ways to reduce the fear of death; and (3) to find some theoretical framework in which death can be viewed more positively as part of life.

The NDE largely accomplishes these goals for the individuals involved. For others, who have not encountered an NDE, knowledge of these experiences may also be helpful, as is suggested in a recent article entitled "Altered States of Consciousness: A Form of Death Education?":

> It is clear that with very little help from the scientific community these goals [the three enumerated above] are being accomplished for a large and growing number of people. Can we afford to ignore the method through which this is happening even if it has been called "unscientific"? . . . Whatever the "explanations" for radically altered states of consciousness, death educators must face the discomfiting fact that a human capacity, viewed negatively within conventional scientific and rational frameworks, seems to produce positive results in terms of adaptive attitudes toward death. Increasingly this appears to be true whether the change originates with systematic attempts to alter the states of consciousness through the spiritual tradition or another, or with an experience of physiological intervention. The physiologically produced state that results in a permanent reorientation toward death may be drug-induced or part of "clinical death," the near-death experiences which have received so much attention recently. . . . If indeed experiences involving non-ordinary modes of perception do alter cultural assumptions about death, and dying, then "unscientific" or no, such experiences further the goals of death educators.[11]

Specifically how these "non-ordinary modes of perception" (in particular, the NDE) will be used to further the goals of death educators is as yet unclear. In this regard, however, I make the following observations. Over the past few years, I have had the opportunity to present the findings of this near-death research to a wide assortment of organizations and gatherings. Invariably, after a presentation, members of the audience will approach me on a one-to-one basis to tell me of their own terminal illness or recent bereavement and further to explain how certain aspects of the presentation have helped them in these situations. From these brief exchanges, I have come to believe that the results of this near-death research may be useful if employed in the counseling of people facing death. Such counseling has recently begun at centers known as hospices, which have been established for the care of the dying patient and his family.

If the NDE is to be used in the context of death education and counseling, then the results of this research will need to be presented in such a fashion as to allow the dying or bereaved person a chance to incorporate this information into his personal belief system. The NDE is not "scientific proof" of life after death and should not be offered as such. Rather, the experience should be presented as a frequently encountered event which suggests that the process of dying may be a calm and peaceful experience for many people. The powerful positive effects of such an experience on the lives of those who have encountered it may serve to comfort others facing similar situations. In effect, the NDE and related implications may serve to accomplish many of the goals set forth by those now working in the field of death and dying.

The "Will to Live"

Earlier in this chapter, we found that the NDE often played a significant role in lessening the fear of death in chronically or terminally ill patients, which in turn assisted these people in living their lives more fully day to day. The NDE did not, however, cause these people to yearn for the hastened arrival of death, but allowed them to accept the reality of their approaching death with equanimity. These positive attitudes toward life and death developed following the NDE, *after* the person had had time to incorporate the significance of his experience into his own life and belief structure. *During* or *immediately following* the NDE, however, many persons expressed a strong desire to remain in the calm and peaceful realm of the NDE and *not* to "return" to the pain and suffering associated with their physical illness. Could this intense desire *not* to "return" to the physical body affect, in any way, the person's actual chances for physical recovery at the moment when death is the closest? That is, is there a psychological component to death, such as a loss of the "will to live," which may interact at times with physical determinants, such as heartbeat, respiration, etc., to determine the outcome of a near-death crisis event? Several clues suggest that such a psychological component to death may indeed exist.

It has been known for quite some time that many individuals can accurately predict the moment of their own physical death, when no other objective medical parameters can be found to support such a prediction. This prediction seems to be based on some psychological intuition known only to the dying person himself. These inexplicable premonitions of death were discussed in an article dealing with terminal illness in the aged in *The Lancet,* a leading British medical journal:

> Seven patients had a premonition of death, and this was communicated to the nurses by such remarks as "Goodbye, I am going" an hour before death. Another thanked the staff nurse who was doing the medicine-rounds for all she had done and said that she would not need tablets any more after tomorrow. A man with congestive cardiac failure thanked all the nurses for their attention the day before his death and a woman with rheumatoid arthritis half an hour before she died asked that her friend should be summoned. There is no doubt that these patients became aware that they were about to die, *but the manner in which this knowledge was imparted to them could not be ascertained.*[12]

Dr. John Hunter Phillips, professor of medicine at Tulane University, published similar observations regarding the "mechanism of death" in elderly patients he had cared for in nursing homes:

> I became interested in the mechanism of death in the elderly while serving in the nursing home, particularly in those patients who predicted that their death was imminent. They would say, "I'm ready to die," and there was very little the physician could do to prevent it. There was usually no obvious lethal disease process evident at the time, the electrocardiogram might be normal, the chest X-ray normal, the screening blood tests all normal, and yet death would occur, usually within 24–48 hours once the positive statement was made. This made me very uneasy, and continues to make me uneasy when I sign the death certificate under the "cause of death." I don't really know *why* they died.[13]

The occasional surgical patient has been known to announce calmly prior to an elective low-risk operation that he "knew" he would not survive the upcoming surgical procedure. This phenomenon was examined in the article "Predilection to Death" by Drs. Weisman and Hackett. The "predilection" patient was described as exhibiting little if any anxiety or depression over his conviction of certain death. Many of these patients would then actually die during the operation. The seriousness of this situation prompted these authors to recommend to their medical colleagues that "psychiatric intervention is indicated when there is a strong conviction of death and little or no somatic disorder to justify it, simply because the *psychological* [italics mine] factor predominates; these are cases of potential 'psychic death' that have been reported in both civilized and primitive communities."[14]

If such psychological factors exist, which can somehow influence our physical survival on an intuitive, nonphysical plane, then is this a "will to live," which, if turned off at the appropriate time, can influence the eventual outcome in a life-death situation? Dr. Lewis Thomas, president of the Sloan-Kettering Cancer Institute and a noted clinician, writes:

> It is not unlikely that there is a pivotal movement at some stage in the body's reaction to injury or disease, maybe in aging as well, when the organism *concedes* that it is finished [i.e., loses the "will to live"] and the time for dying is at hand, and at this moment the events that lead to death are launched as a coordinated mechanism. Functions are then shut off, in sequence, irreversibly, and while this is going on, a neural mechanism, held ready for this occasion, is switched on, so that the perception in consciousness becomes that of . . . the resuscitated patient who fell dead with cardiac standstill in front of a Los Angeles hospital, was carried inside to have his heart started again by electric shock, and remembered his wonderment at the agitation of people around his stretcher at such a time of tranquility. If there should be such a mechanism for the process of dying, we should be on the lookout for pathology in its operation on the assumption that any intricate mechanism can slip up and be turned on inappropriately. Perhaps something like this happens in the well-documented cases of death with witchcraft and hexing.[15]

Cases of witchcraft and hexing are common among the primitive tribes of the Australian aborigines. Dr. Walter B. Cannon examined these practices in an article entitled "Voodoo Death" in the *American Anthropologist*. Dr. Cannon cites the following example of hexing through the pointing of a bone by a medicine man ("bone-pointing syndrome"):

> The man who discovers that he is being boned by an enemy is, indeed, a pitiable sight. He stands aghast, with his eyes staring at the treacherous pointer, and with his hands lifted as though to ward off the lethal medium, which he imagines is pouring into his body. His cheeks blanch and his eyes become glassy and the expression of his face becomes horribly distorted. . . . He attempts to shriek but usually the sound chokes in his throat, and all that one might see is froth at his mouth. His body begins to tremble and the muscles twist involuntarily. He sways backwards and falls to the ground, and after a short time appears to be in a swoon; but soon after he writhes as if in mortal agony, and, covering his face with his hands, begins to moan. After a while he becomes very composed and crawls to his wurley. From this time onwards he sickens and frets, refusing to eat and keeping aloof from the daily affairs of the tribe. Unless help is forthcoming in the shape of a counter-charm administered by the hands of the Nangarri, or medicine-man, his death is only a matter of a comparatively short time. If the coming of the medicine-man is opportune he might be saved.[16]

Dr. Cannon presented similar reports of "psychic death" from battlefield physicians during World War I. According to these reports, soldiers would occasionally lapse into an extended period of shock and then die despite intensive medical attention. These deaths would result from severe *psychological* trauma from some battlefield incident which caused no significant *physical* injury as determined at autopsy.

In the experimental laboratory, what well may be an animal counterpart to the human syndrome of "psychic death" was uncovered quite by accident at Johns Hopkins University. Dr. Curt Richter found that laboratory rats who had had their whiskers clipped were particularly susceptible to sudden death when placed in a tank of water. Normal rats could swim up to seventy-two hours, while their dewhiskered counterparts often gave up, died, and sank to the bottom within minutes. If, however, the dewhiskered rats were rescued at the last moment from drowning, rapid recovery was the rule. When retested in the same tank, these dewhiskered rats who had previously been rescued could then swim as long as the normal controls. The combination of deep water and no whiskers was a rapidly lethal condition; but once rescued, the "spell" was broken and survival time in the tank for the dewhiskered rats became normal.[17]

Thus, in these cases involving the primitive tribesman, the battlefield soldier and the laboratory rat, there appears to be the inappropriate switching on of a "mechanism for the process of dying" at a time when physiologically the body is in no danger of death. In short, the "will to live" seems to have been temporarily lost or shut off, resulting in physical death initiated by a nonphysical cause.

Turning now to the NDE, is it possible that this powerful experience could influence our will to live at the critical moment when death hangs in the balance? Could one's strong desire *not* to "come back" affect the ultimate outcome of a near-death crisis event? One physician who had had an NDE himself told me that he was firmly convinced that the NDE could have such an effect and that he now takes this into account each time a patient of his becomes seriously ill and near death:

> [During my NDE] I didn't want to come back because the tranquility and peacefulness is so great. Then they began some resuscitation measures and it didn't take long to bring me around, but during this I did not want to come back. . . . Since I've had this, I've had two patients, one who really exsanguinated and we had a little trouble getting the blood started and I flat out told her, "_____, you cannot die." And I really think this has an effect on bringing them back, because they don't want to come back. I didn't want to come back . . .

then after I got back and I've been here, I realize how lucky I was that I had this happen to me. (I–49)

Others also felt that during their NDE they were faced with the very real decision to die or to live. One man had the following thoughts during an extended cardiac arrest:

Well, I wanted to go on but I didn't want to go. I didn't want to leave my wife and my kids. But I believe if it hadn't been for my wife and kids, I would have fought to have gotten on up there. It seemed like I had to make a decision. (I–63–1)

A man expressed concern over whether he would "elect to come back" if again faced with this decision during an NDE:

I don't fear dying anymore except for leaving my family. . . . And I'm afraid if I get to dying, and I get to a point, I may just elect to travel on and that's what worries me most of all. I don't know how strong I'd be. If I got in that position again, I don't know whether I'd elect to come back or go on. . . . I think your *inner being* controls your health to a large extent and if you want to go on, you can. You see so much of that in people who just give up. (I–5)

Another man admitted having thoughts of "giving in" to his illness following his NDE because of the stark contrast between the peace and painlessness of the NDE and the pain and suffering of an extended convalescence. The unrelenting tenacity of the intern caring for him at the time kept him "pushing" to get well:

After this [NDE] happened, I didn't have any fear of dying, and why they were able to keep me alive or how they did it, I have no idea at all. I didn't fight against it [death] mainly because the doctor kept on fighting against it. He said, "You get as mad as you want to, angry, cuss us all out. You'll live. You've got to fight now. You've got to keep hanging in. It's going to get harder." And it did. And it was that time that I had time to think. . . . It was this time that I seriously considered signing a paper or getting my family to intercede when I was in this coma. But I wasn't staying in the coma long enough to justify any doctor going along with it. . . . I felt so bad, but every time I started thinking negative, the doctor was there. I think he knew what I was thinking before I did, I don't know. He had to keep pushing me to get well. . . . All I know is my doctor wanted to get me well and I don't know whether he hypnotized me or not. . . . I really couldn't understand it because I don't think he [the doctor] understood where I'd been [during the NDE]. I never told him. I haven't told him to this day. (I-23)

In short, some evidence suggests that there may be a strong *psychological* component—a "will to live"—which is involved in determining the *physical* outcome of a life-death situation. Many persons, during or immediately following their NDE, have a strong desire to *return* to the peaceful and painless realm encountered during the experience. Since these people strongly associated their NDE with death itself, their desire to return to the experience was the psychological equivalent of quite simply *wanting to die*. Thus it is possible that this desire for death (or loss of the will to live) may actually influence the physical outcome of many near-death crisis events during those few moments when life or death hangs in the balance.

This reasoning may also apply in the opposite way to those who, during their NDE, actively yearned to "return" to their physical body to complete some "unfinished business." This psychological impetus to continue physical life may have contributed to their *successful* resuscitation and recovery from the near-death crisis event. Needless to say, the *extent* to which these psychological drives actually affect the physical outcome of the near-death situation is difficult to assess. It is likely, however, that the outcome of many life-death situations is affected not only by its physical determinants but by a complex interaction of psychophysical factors, including the NDE and one's will to live.

10

Explanations

In the supercharged atmosphere of today's fantasy market, the reentry trip, the coming back down to earth can be disppointing. The fun is over, but we all may be better off if we start to prepare for the descent from the giddy heights of uncritical thought. If history is any teacher then the current fascination with "life after life" will give way as some new mind trip arises to take its place—as it encounters some hard knocks against reality.[1]

Robert Kastenbaum, Ph.D.
Professor of Psychology
University of Massachusetts

IN THE SPRING of 1976, when I first read *Life After Life,* I, like Dr. Kastenbaum, identified these experiences as part of "some new mind trip" designed to titillate the imagination of the public and the media. And titillate it did: personal testimonials of other claiming similar "afterlife voyages" became commonplace in newspapers and magazines; headlines on popular tabloids regularly announced that "proof" of life after death had finally arrived; weekly contests with cash prizes were run for the best "out-of-body" experience submitted; millions of dollars were spent publicizing a "documentary" movie portraying the NDE with theatrical techniques developed from science fiction thrillers; and dozens of books were published to cash in on the lucrative sensationalism of the subject.

Confronted with this media "bandwagon" precipitated by Raymond Moody's book, the medical community fired back. The following excerpt from the *Journal of the American Medical Association*, November 23, 1979, was typical of this response:

> ... people who undergo these "death experiences" are suffering from a hypoxic state, during which they try to deal psychologically with the anxieties provoked by medical procedures and talk. ... We are dealing here with the fantasy of death. ... It establishes the certainty of heaven, where one can have a reunion with people from the past, and where one can have a life after death. That it answers so many puzzles of mankind and creates a bridge between science and religion makes it a tempting concept for speculation. It is for this very reason that the physician must be especially wary of accepting religious belief as scientific data.[2]

In the above medical journal article, whose title is "To Sleep, Perchance to Dream ..." Dr. Richard S. Blacher expressed feelings similar to mine when I began my research. Four years later, however, my sentiments about the NDE had changed, as evidenced by my response to Dr. Blacher's article, published in the July 4, 1980, issue of the *Journal of the American Medical Association*:

> I have recently conducted a systematic investigation of these experiences. ... Like Dr. Blacher, I have concluded that these experiences are not by themselves prima facie evidence of life after death ... [but] Sensational after-life proclamations by prophets in the lay media cannot be countered with scientific assertions based on anecdotal experience. Such seems to be the case [with Dr. Blacher and his several medical explanations of the experience]. ... Dr. Blacher points out that "the physician must be especially wary of accepting religious belief as scientific data." I might add that equal caution should be exercised in accepting scientific belief as scientific data.[3]

The reasons for my wariness in accepting "scientific belief as scientific data" as an explanation for the NDE will be the focus of this chapter.

In considering an explanation for the NDE, let us first reexamine the meaning of a near-death crisis event as it applies to this study. In Chapter 1 we defined the near-death crisis event as any medical situation in which the patient had been rendered unconscious and physically near death—that is, in any bodily state that would reasonably be expected to result in irreversible biological death in the majority of instances and would demand (if available) urgent medical attention. Unconsciousness was defined as any specific period of time during which the person lost all subjective awareness of environment and self—i.e., blacking out. The fact that the person had indeed been physically "near death" was verified in almost every case by a source other than the individual under study (medical records, etc.). Whether or not unconsciousness had been associated with this episode of physical near-death, however, could not be verified for reasons stated in Chapter 1. Thus the state of unconsciousness became a subjective assessment by the individual experiencing the event. To others at the time, he may have appeared totally unconscious when physically near death and it may logically have been assumed that under the circumstances (i.e., total arrest of the heart) he would have been unconscious, but the final determination was left to the person himself.

Suppose, now, that this person whom we had assumed to be unconscious was in fact not unconscious at all. While I was conducting a Medical Grand Rounds on Near Death Experiences at the University of Florida in 1978, a professor of medicine raised the following point:

> We have all resuscitated patients who have appeared dead at the time but who later could tell us of our conversation during the period of resuscitation. How do you know that these people who are describing an "accurate" near-death experience are not just hearing the conversation while *semiconscious* at the time and later conjuring up a visual image in their mind of what went on?

Semiconscious State

There is no doubt that the sense of hearing is one of the last things to go as a person loses consciousness. A severely injured or sick individual can lie motionless with closed eyes and barely perceptible vital signs but still hear what is being said. A dramatic example of just such an occurrence is recounted below:

> . . . a respected supervisory nurse recalled her own admission to the emergency room. She was one of four people severely injured in an automobile accident . . . she could not utter a sound or move her body. However, like many people in a traumatized state, she could hear the sounds and voices around her. "This one is gone," a voice was saying. "Let's get to one of the others next." The nurse realized that she was the one who had just been dismissed as dead. Her response: "I became furious—just plain furious! No way was I going to stay dead for them! . . . In my mind, I kept

shouting 'I'm not dead yet, you bastards!' I'm not sure if those words came across to them, but some sounds did get out."[4]

Could, then, the autoscopic "visual" descriptions in the NDE be merely the piecing together of aurally perceived information by a semi-conscious patient (mistakenly presumed unconscious) into an accurate "mental picture" of ongoing events, as suggested by the professor of medicine? Several bits of evidence suggest that this is not so.

First, as discussed in Chapter 6, hypnotic regression of patients who had been under general anesthesia during a major operation has uncovered their memory of conversations among the attending doctors and nurses, but not of visual impressions. An anesthetized or semi-anesthetized individual who is registering spoken words is in a situation similar to that of the semiconscious, ill or injured person lying motionless with eyes closed but still listening to ongoing events. Such recall in the surgical situation, even when frightening, has been reported by these patients to be an aurally perceived event that is quite unlike the detailed "visual" impression of an NDE. Moreover, the example of the supervisory nurse lying semiconscious in a nonsurgical setting further supports the contention that aurally perceived knowledge in the semiconscious patient will later be recalled as a verbal, nonvisual impression.

Second, if the person is describing an autoscopic NDE based on semiconscious perceptions at the point of near-death (hearing, feeling, etc.), then his situation can be compared in many respects to that of the semiconscious patient undergoing elective cardioversion. In cardioversion, an electric shock is applied to the chest to normalize heart rhythm. This procedure is often done on an elective basis to correct abnormal heart rhythms. Cardioversion, as you may recall, is also used during most cardiac resuscitations to correct life-threatening rhythm disturbances of the heart. In the elective situation, the patient is given a medication (e.g., intravenous Valium) to dull his senses and render him semiconscious, so as to minimize the pain of the electric shock. In this semiconscious state, however, the patient can sometimes still hear nearby conversation and recall the sensations associated with the shock itself; for example: "It's like having everything torn out of your insides"; "like a minor tremor which pulls one's body apart from the inside"; "The shocks were like a big boom."[5] One would expect similar sensations to be reported by the near-death patient *if* indeed he is merely semiconscious during his NDE. But the report of the cardioversion experience is much different following an NDE:

I could see myself jolt, but again it didn't hurt like an electric shock should hurt. . . . I wasn't hurting, I wasn't anxious. . . . I had no pain. (I–32)

They were rubbing those things together and then I bounced off the table . . . I came off the table about nine to ten inches, I seemed to arch. . . . [While watching] I seemed to be in a very peaceful state. (I–8)

I thought they had given my body too much voltage because my body jumped about two feet off the table. . . . [While watching, I felt] floating, soft, easy, comfortable, nothing wrong. (I–19)

Thus the cardioversion procedure during an NDE is associated with a painless, pleasant sensation, while the same electric shock is a distinctly uncomfortable moment when recalled by the electively cardioverted patient in the semiconscious state.

Third, several persons during their near-death crisis could clearly distinguish between their semiconscious auditory perception of nearby conversation and the *subsequent* appearance of a "visually" perceived NDE:

They had sounded a Code 99 because of the instability of the heartbeat and so forth. So I was describing to them what was happening and I told them that my eyes were going slowly out and then coming back as my heart beats again. I was describing this to them because I thought it would be interesting to the people listening. And then the eyes went out for good and I was in total blackness and I didn't have any ability to move but I could hear well and understand. I heard them talk and I heard the guy say my pressure was zero and who it was and I heard Dr. J say, "Shall we try to get a pulse?" And I wanted to answer and tried to answer but couldn't. . . . That's when I had the experience [NDE]—*After* sound and all had gone and I couldn't hear anymore. (I–3)

Another man had experienced both the semiconscious state with preserved auditory perception and unconsciousness associated with an NDE, and could compare the two situations:

Several years back, I was in an auto accident. . . . I was laying there [emergency room] and I could hear two nurses there and they were trying to get my blood pressure. One says to the other, "You know, I can't get a reading on this," or something like that, and she said, "Well, try the other one." And I heard all this and I knew they were there but I couldn't communicate with them. I heard the intercom, just as plain as day: "Any doctor on the floor report to the emergency room immediately." And I was just laying there thinking: Boy, somebody's in bad shape in the emergency room. I wasn't realizing it was me. . . . I don't know what he [the doctor] done to me, but he brought me back to and it felt like somebody had poured a hot pot of water on top of me. . . . And he [the doctor] said, "Well, you had no vital signs or nothing." But I didn't see nothing. I just heard. This other time with the cardiac arrest [and NDE], I was looking down from the ceiling and there were no ifs, ands or buts about it. (I–14)

These two examples demonstrate that semiconscious auditory perception and perceptions associated with the NDE can clearly be differentiated by persons who have experienced both.

Finally, a few NDEs of an autoscopic nature were reported by individuals who had been unconscious and near death while no one else was present. In these cases, semiconscious perception of verbal information would have been virtually impossible, since no one had been present to supply it.

It thus appears unlikely that the autoscopic NDE can be attributed to *semiconscious* auditory perception of events during the near-death crisis event, as suggested by the Florida professor of medicine. But how do we know that people reporting an NDE are not consciously fabricating their experience? Could they just be "making it all up"?

Conscious Fabrication

I must admit that when I first read *Life After Life,* I felt these experiences were either fabrications by persons who had taken advantage of the author, Dr. Raymond Moody, or were embellishments by Moody himself to produce a best-selling book. Five years and 116 interviews later, I am convinced that my original suspicions about this were wrong, for many reasons.

First, the interviewing procedure, involving a large number of patients, offered little, if any, reward for describing an NDE. My colleague Sarah Kreutziger and I were quite careful to approach these patients as if a routine medical history were being taken. Our interest in the NDE was not revealed until late in the interview. Each person was informed that his identity would not be disclosed when the results of our investigation were announced. If there was any bias on my part during the first year or so of the study, it was weighted toward a disbelief in the validity of these near-death reports. (I was recently reminded of this fact by a patient I interviewed early in the study. She spontaneously remarked during a conversation we had four years later, "You seemed to be out to mainly disprove the experience as much as anything when I talked with you the first time.") It also became obvious early in the study that in spite of the extraordinary nature of these recollections, the persons themselves seemed truly to believe in the reality of their experience and had actually protected it from the ridicule of others. This was not an experience that was freely being described for its sensational effect. In fact, when these people were asked, "Have you told many others of your experience?" they would respond characteristically:

Only a few, when they seem receptive. I don't talk about it too much. People begin to think you're a little nuts. (I-47)

Oh, a few. A lot of them laugh at me and make fun of me, so I just don't bother telling them anymore. They think you're crazy or something. (I-25)

No. I thought they would think I was crazy. (I-14)

No, sir, You're the only person. . . . People will think I'm crazy. . . . I've lived with this thing for three years now and I haven't told anyone because I don't want them putting the straitjacket on me. . . . It's real as hell. (I-19)

Second, through my medical involvement in the lives of many of these patients, I could often detect a change in the attitudes and beliefs of those who had told me of their NDE. A deepening of religious beliefs, a changing of vocational interests (e.g., becoming hospital volunteers) and a focusing on more humanitarian concerns were common developments. Moreover, the patient's outlook on life was often transformed in such a way as to allow him to cope more successfully with the day-to-day trials of a critical medical illness. (See detailed discussion in chapter 9.) When asked about these observable changes in his or her life style and beliefs, each person would invariably attribute the change in some way to the NDE. Thus the NDE became a powerful, motivating influence for many who had encountered it. Such an effect in itself provided indirect evidence that the NDE was not a consciously fabricated event.

Third, at the start of the study, I anticipated a wide variation in the structure and content of these NDEs, since I suspected that the experience would largely reflect personal dreams and fantasies. As the interviewing progressed, however, it became evident that all the experiences generally conformed to one of three basic patterns—the autoscopic, the transcendental or the combined NDE. In addition, this consistency did not appear to have resulted from fabricated stories that had been conveniently patterned after a common model experience, because (1) many of the subjects were not aware of the NDE prior to their own encounter; (2) a major portion of the interviewing was done at a time when *Life After Life* and related media releases were not general knowledge in the rural populations of northern Florida (where most of the subjects resided); and (3) when subjects *were* aware of the NDE from other sources prior to the interview, they would often remark how the details of their own experience had differed from the ones reported by others. For instance, a 57-year-old construction worker from north Georgia had this to say about the other reports:

A: What do you think about what other people have written about these experiences?

S: I think that about 95 percent of it is just plain bullshit. That's what I believe when they talk about their dear old auntie, their daddy, and so on. I know it's fraud. I think anybody with common sense would realize that. How could their dead auntie, their pet dogs, and so on meet them in their physical body when their physical bodies are laying on earth in a ditch covered with dirt? That shows you that somebody's lying right there. Also, these dreams are so detailed and long you'd have to be dead and rotten by the time you could have such an experience. You have to be flesh dropping off your bones to have that kind of a trip.

A: Do you believe your experience was real?

S: Yes. Sure. I do now, personally. It was a real experience to me. . . .

A: What would you have thought if someone else had told you of an experience similar to yours before you had had your own?

S: I would have thought he was full of crap. (I-5)

For this man as for others in this study, "seeing was believing."

Finally, my initial skepticism concerning the veracity of these reports prompted me to pay particular attention to the details of the medical procedures purportedly seen during the autoscopic NDEs. When such details were reported, every effort was made either to verify or to disprove them, using sources independent of the interviewee. As it turned out, such verification was available in many cases,* leading me to the conclusion that the NDE had to be something more than a simple fabrication.

Assuming, then, that the reported experience is not a consciously fabricated event, let us examine some other explanations that have been proposed for the NDE.

Subconscious Fabrication

> Our own death is indeed unimaginable, and whenever we make the attempt to imagine it we can perceive that we really survive as spectators. Hence . . . at bottom no one believes in his own death, or to put the same thing in another way, in the unconscious every one of us is convinced of his own immortality.[6]
>
> Sigmund Freud, 1915

Could the NDE have been formulated out of a subconscious human need to overcome the threat of extinction and to survive ultimately as a "spectator," as suggested here by Freud? Certainly the "spectator" quality of the autoscopic NDE would fit conceptually with Freud's contention. In fact, many persons even described their experience as if they had been a spectator or a disinterested observer. If the NDE were such a subconscious fabrication, however, I would expect it to appear each time the person's ego perceived a serious threat of death. That is, if the person's ego found it necessary to fabricate the NDE for "protection" during one near-death crisis event, then this protection should appear each time a similar or more serious near-death crisis was perceived by that person. This was not the case. Several persons in this study encountered multiple separate near-death crisis events but could later recall only one NDE. Moreover, the crisis event that *was* associated with an NDE was sometimes the one perceived by the person (and documented in the medical record) to have been the *least* life-threatening (that is, the medical crisis during which the person was in the least danger of dying). This finding suggests that if the NDE results from a subconscious need to survive bodily death, then this need is being manifested in an inconsistent fashion.

In addition, we found other persons who *did* encounter multiple NDEs during recurrent near-death crises. Although the descriptions of these separately occurring NDEs sometimes varied, each conformed to

* See Chapter 7.

one of the three basic patterns of the NDE—the autoscopic, the transcendental or the combined. One man, for instance, reported a typical transcendental NDE following a cardiac arrest in 1969:

> When I was down under I had this weird deal. . . . It seemed like my mother who had died when I was eight years old, and she was upon a hill and there was a big bright light behind. I was crawling to get up there and she had her hand out to me. Seemed like I was just inches from touching her hand and I started sliding back down the hill and I guess that's when I woke up.* (I–63–1)

Nine years later, this same man reported a purely autoscopic NDE during another cardiac arrest:

> I remember I got up on the side of the bed and heaved and that's the last I remember until I was floating right up on the ceiling. . . . I was laying in the bed with the sides up, and the doctor was here and my wife was here and there was somebody here, I don't know whether it was a corpsman or what. The nurse was on this side of the bed with that machine. She picked up them shocker things and put one there and one right there [pointing to appropriate places on chest] and I seen my body flop like that and I was back. (I–63–2)

Using Freud's theory of subconscious fabrication, why should the subconscious mind of the man above find it necessary to formulate two completely different patterns of "ego survival" on two separate but similar occasions? Had his subconscious needs changed over the nine years that separated his two experiences? Perhaps. But then why should these two totally different experiences conform, in a larger sense, to one of three general patterns of the NDE reported by other individuals? My feeling is that the NDE is not so much a protective response of one's subconscious mind as it is a basic human experience. Viewed in this way, the NDE becomes more of a natural phenomenological process, which can be entered into and modified in certain individual ways, but which maintains a basic structure independent of the whims and fantasies present in the subconscious minds of various individuals.

Depersonalization

Depersonalization is a frequent reaction to life-threatening danger. As an adaptive pattern of the nervous system it alerts the organism to its threatening environment while holding potentially disorganizing emotion in check. As a psychological mechanism it defends the endangered personality against the threat of death and at the same time, initiates an integration of that reality. And, as a meaningful experience, a mystical elaboration of the phenomenon may achieve spiritual significance. This type of encounter with death may be followed by a sense of rebirth.[7]

Russell Noyes, M.D.
Professor of Psychiatry
University of Iowa

Freud's concept that serious contemplation of death leads to a fantasy of survival as a spectator is related in some ways to the conclusions reached by Dr. Russell Noyes, who has conducted extensive research into the subjective experiences reported by individuals who have confronted the sudden psychological reality of their own physical death. For example, suppose you are driving a car and suddenly lose control. You watch helplessly as your car leaves the roadbed at a high rate of speed and heads directly for a stone wall. You become acutely aware that death is imminent and unavoidable. The crash occurs but miraculously you survive without serious injury. You later recall that in the few fleeting moments prior to impact, a series of strange subjective impressions had raced through your mind—impressions that Dr. Noyes has labeled "depersonalization in the face of life-threatening danger."

One such experience was reported to Dr. Noyes by a young race car driver who had been thrown thirty feet in the air during a racing accident. At no time during the accident, however, was the driver unconscious or *physically* near death:

"As soon as I saw him I knew I was going to hit him. . . . It seemed like the whole thing took forever. Everything was in slow motion and it seemed to me like I was a player on a stage and could see myself tumbling over and over in the car. It was as though I sat in the stands and saw it all happening . . . but I was not frightened. . . . Everything was so strange. . . . The whole experience was like a dream but at no time did I lose my sense of where I was. . . . I was like floating on air. . . . Finally, the car pancaked itself on the track and I was jolted back to reality."[8]

From experiences such as this, Dr. Noyes identified several characteristics of the syndrome of "depersonalization in the face of life-threatening danger." These are an altered perception of time, an increased speed of thoughts, a sense of detachment, a feeling of unreality, a lack of emotion, a revival of memories, a sense of harmony or unity with the universe, and sharper vision or hearing.

Because Dr. Noyes interpreted these experiences as being a psychological reaction to an overwhelming threat of death, he felt that the endangered person must clearly perceive the imminence of his own death *before* the syndrome of depersonalization could develop. In other words, the perception of death serves as a trigger for the depersonalization reaction. Continuing with Dr. Noyes:

> Subjective reports suggest that the chief prerequisite to their [NDEs'] full development is the *perception* [italics mine] of imminent death. . . . [Otherwise] victims of cardiac arrests may not have such experiences unless convinced of their closeness to death.[9]

Dr. Richard Blacher, in the article referred to earlier in this chapter, also felt that a person's *awareness* of death was the key ingredient in the development of a subjective experience at the point of near-death:

> First, it is clear that these experiences [NDEs] occur only when there is a *gradual* [italics mine] cardiac arrest. Such experiences do not occur with Stokes-Adams attacks [sudden loss of consciousness *without warning* from stoppage of the heart], during which the patient describes no mental sensations with the sudden stopping of the heart.[10]

Thus, according to both Dr. Noyes and Dr. Blacher, if a person is not afforded a chance to perceive the imminence of his own "sudden death," then no subjective experience (such as an NDE) would be expected to evolve.

In my study of NDEs, I found several cases that involved the sudden loss of consciousness with stoppage of the heart from the Stokes-Adams syndrome, referred to by Dr. Blacher. Moreover, some of these persons described an NDE that had developed after the loss of consciousness from the attack. One such case was of a middle-aged farmer from north Florida whom I admitted to the Gainesville VA Hospital with an acute heart attack and transient episodes of complete heart block (total stoppage of the heart). While I was making preparations for emergency placement of a cardiac pacemaker, he had several episodes of complete heart block, during which he would suddenly lose consciousness in the middle of a sentence. A grand mal seizure would develop during those episodes which were more prolonged. After placement of the pacemaker, I interviewed this man, and he told me of the following NDE, which occurred before he was brought to the hospital:

> I was walking across the parking lot to get into my car. . . . I passed out. I don't recall hitting the ground. The next thing I do recall was that I was above the cars, floating. I had a real funny sensation, a

floating sensation. I was actually looking down on my own body, with four or five men running toward me. I could hear and understand what these men were saying. To me, it was a real funny feeling. I had no pain whatsoever. I didn't feel any pain. Then the next thing, when I came to my senses, I was in my body and I had pain on the back of my head where I had hit the concrete. (I–20)

This man had developed an autoscopic NDE even though there had been no time for him to appreciate fully the imminence of his "death" in a psychological sense.

Another difference between Dr. Noyes's study and my own was in subject selection criteria. Dr. Noyes focused primarily on persons who had been psychologically but not physically near death. However, he did interview a small group of subjects who were both psychologically and physically endangered (i.e., "the seriously ill group"), but found the reports of the latter group to be significantly different from those of persons who had escaped only "psychological" near-death:

> the seriously ill group was clearly deviant showing a higher frequency for most items (evaluated in these experiences) and doubling for many. The subjects in this group also differed with regard to the circumstances of their experiences. Eighty percent believed themselves about to die, 71% lost consciousness and only 50% made efforts to rescue themselves. Consequently, the responses of this relatively small group were eliminated from further analysis.[11]

In another paper, Dr. Noyes reemphasizes these differences between experiences reported by psychologically and physically threatened subjects:

> It seems important to note that there are a great variety of near-death experiences. Those studied by the author [Noyes] were reported by persons who were psychologically—but not necessarily physically—close to death. A different kind of experience has been described by persons who narrowly escaped death from physical illness, cardiac arrest, etc.[12]

Thus Dr. Noyes's theory of "depersonalization in the face of life-threatening danger" is a hypothesis based on the experiences of persons perceiving a *psychological* near-death. Persons who narrowly escape *physical* death (such as those in my study) describe a different type of experience, which often develops without a clear premonitory perception of imminent death. Thus the psychological theory of depersonalization does not account for the NDE reported by persons surviving an episode of unconsciousness and physical near-death.

Autoscopic Hallucination

The perplexing experience of autoscopy, i.e., of seeing one's own "self," or one's "double," has always puzzled and fascinated the human imagination and has been known to all races from time immemorial.

A. Lukianowicz, M.D.
Barrow Hospital
Bristol, England

So began a report entitled "Autoscopic Phenomena" in the *A.M.A. Archives of Neurology and Psychiatry,* August 1958.[13] In it, the author gives several case histories of patients suffering from autoscopic hallucinations. To my knowledge, Dr. Lukianowicz has not used the findings in his report as a possible explanation for the NDE. Many other physicians have approached me with this possibility, however, thus prompting the following analysis.

"Autoscopy" simply means self-visualization. The type of autoscopy, however, found in autoscopic hallucinations and the NDE is quite different. According to Dr. Lukianowicz, the autoscopic hallucination is a rare psychiatric disorder, seen primarily in patients with depression, epilepsy or schizophrenia. Characteristically, these patients will suddenly and without warning perceive a visual image of their own face or upper trunk projected a few feet in front of their physical bodies. This image is usually colorless and transparent and will often imitate all movements and facial expressions of the "original"—as if the subject were looking in a mirror. This situation is perceived by the patient as "unreal" and will often leave him sad and weary. One such encounter was reported by Lukianowicz as follows:

> . . . in the twilight of the late afternoon she noticed a lady in front of her. Mrs. A lifted her right hand to turn on the light. The strange lady made the same movement with her left hand, and thus their hands met. . . . Mrs. A. felt cold in her right hand and experienced a sensation as if all blood ran out of her hand. Under the electric light she noticed that the stranger wore an exact replica of her own coat, hat, and veil . . . she began to undress and took off her veil, her hat, and her coat. The lady in black did exactly the same. Only then did Mrs. A. become aware that it was she herself staring at herself, as if in a mirror, and mimicking her own movements and gestures.[14]

Direct interaction between the image and its "original" was sometimes described:

[the patient would see] an image of his own face "as if looking at it in a mirror." This phantom face would imitate all his facial expressions and D. (patient) would frequently "play with it," forcing it to copy his mimicking. The patient's attitude toward his double was overtly sadistic. . . . For instance, he would often strike the phantom on its head, and the specter was not able to avoid the blows.[15]

In comparing the autoscopic description found in the hallucinatory encounter and the NDE, several differences are evident. Unlike the NDE, autoscopic hallucinations (1) consist of the physical body ("original") perceiving the projected image ("double"); (2) involve direct interaction between the "original" and the "double"; (3) are perceived as being unreal; and (4) commonly evoke negative emotions. For these reasons, the autoscopic hallucination does not appear to be a plausible explanation for the NDE.

Dreams

Dreams may appear to be quite real at the time of their occurrence. What separates the near-death experience from a vivid dream encounter?[16]

A professor of medicine

Dreams are common human experiences. Many of the near-death subjects interviewed in this study described the regular occurrence of nighttime dreams and often compared these dreams to their NDEs:

I thought: Gee, what a terrible dream that was! But it wasn't a dream. It was too real and it happened. (I–55s)

S: It's like a dream. You're detached from the thing and watching it as a bystander.
A: But the things you are "dreaming" are really happening?
S: Oh, yes. They are real. (I–32)

It's reality. I know for myself that I didn't experience no fantasy. There was no so-called dream or nothing. These things really happened to me. It happened. I know. I went through it. Even though I was in a blackout stage I know myself that I went through it. (I–15)

I've had a lot of dreams and it wasn't like any dream that I had had. It was real. It was so real. And that peace, the peace made the difference from a dream, and I dream a lot. (I–59)

This emphasis on the reality of the NDE versus the unreality of the dream was made by all subjects who were asked to compare these two conditions. Perceiving the unreality of a dream experience was thought by Freud to afford the dreamer a reassurance "aimed at reducing the importance of what has just been experienced and at making it possible to tolerate what is to follow."[17] In other words, the unreality of a dream usually provides for the continuance of sleep despite potentially disrupting perceptions. The NDE, however, is perceived as stark reality both during the experience and later in reflection. In addition, the extreme variability of dream content from person to person and from night to night contrasts with the consistency of events in the NDE. It is thus unlikely that the NDE can be explained as being a dream.

Prior Expectation

Human nature being what it is—human—many of us will continue to deny the unknown [in this case, death], romanticizing it as is done so frequently in opera (*Liebestod*) and in stories of "lovers leap" and "going to his/her reward." Of course, there are the old, the tired, and the religious who look forward to "going home again" (to the arms of Jesus).[18]

Nathan Schnaper, M.D.
Professor of Psychiatry
University of Maryland

Is the NDE a fulfillment of prior expectations based on a personal romanticizing of death, as suggested by Dr. Schnaper? One approach to answering this question would be to examine the expectations and fantasies of persons regarding their own death prior to their NDE. This was done in many cases by asking during the interview: "What would you have thought if someone else had told you of an experience similar to the one you had had, but before you had had your own experience?" The following responses to this question were typical:

I had never thought they [other people] were sincere about it. You know, you hear fantasies and you tend to believe them but in a state of mind you know that, well, they're lying about it. (I–15)

I've heard of them [NDE] and I've laughed at them. (I–44)

I probably would have reacted like everyone else and sort of snickered. (I–60)

I thought they [other people] were nuts. I completely discredited it.
I never believed it. (I–14)

Other persons were asked to comment on their personal concept of
death prior to their NDE. One man put it this way:

A: What do you think this experience [NDE] represented?
S: I think I was dead for a while. I mean at least spirit-wise. I
   think my spirit left my body for a while. If that's death, it's not
   bad.
A: Did you think that death would be this way before you had
   this experience?
S: No. Before I had this experience I figured when you're dead,
   you're dead. That's all. I believe now that your spirit does
   leave your body.
A: So this has changed your outlook on death?
S: Oh, yeah! (I–63–1)

Another man—an American soldier in Vietnam at the time
(1969)—had been nearly fatally wounded on the battlefield. Prior to his
injury, he had carefully considered what it would be like to die. Lying
semiconscious on the battlefield, in shock from losing both legs and an
arm, he reviewed in his mind what he had "been told" about the "three
stages" of death and began comparing these three stages to what he was
feeling at the moment:

When I came down and hit the ground, I remember sitting up and I
saw my right arm gone and my right leg gone and my left leg was
laying off to the left side. I fell back and I remember that very
clearly. I couldn't get back up. . . . I had always heard and had always been told that if you die, you really go through three stages
before death sets in. The first one is that you lose your sight. I
remember I couldn't open my eyes and I couldn't see. The second
stage would be that you would always lose feeling, you would not
feel pain or pressure. I couldn't feel pain. The third part would be
that you would go into total relaxation and it's over with. Laying
there, I was thinking about these three things and I realized realis-
tically what I perceived was dying or being dead. (I–68)

Up to this point, his death was proceeding according to expectations. But
then another stage unfolded:

I'm laying there on the battlefield and I came out of my body and I
perceived me laying on the ground with three limbs gone. I knew it
was me. I recognized me. I could not tell what shape or form I was
in. . . . I didn't perceive life in the form on the ground. I perceived
life in me outside the body. I wasn't a triple amputee. I was a shape
and a form, but I don't know what I was. I could not see appen-
dages. I perceived I was in the air, though. I was not touching
ground. It was almost like I floated.

Thus, from these examples, it does not appear that the NDE can be
directly attributed to a fulfillment of personal expectations of what death
(or near-death) would be like.

Drug-Induced Delusion or Hallucination

Vivid hallucinatory and delusional experiences are encountered by
patients during severe medical illness and can be easily attributed to
the painkilling narcotics administered to these patients. How is the
near-death experience any different?[19]
            A physician in the audience of my lecture on NDEs, 1978
            Albany Medical College
            Albany, New York

Several drugs that have been associated with delusional or hallucinatory experiences are commonly used during an acute medical crisis.
Morphine sulfate, for example, is quite effective in relieving the chest
pain from a heart attack or the pulmonary congestion from acute heart
failure. At least some persons who reported an NDE in this study were
under the influence of morphine or a similar hallucinogen at the time of
their near-death crisis event. Certainly drug-induced hallucinations as a
cause for the NDE deserve consideration.

Medical studies of the content and structure of drug-induced hallucinations have found these experiences to be highly variable and idio-
syncratic. The administration of narcotics for either medicinal or illicit
purposes can be associated with a "high" of euphoria and bliss or a "bad
trip" of terrifyingly distorted perceptions. The latter type of experience
was reported to me by a man who was convinced that he had encountered a "bad NDE" while under sedation with opiates after a major
operation:

Well, when I was coming out from under surgery, I had a vision
that my one doctor came and sat on the edge of the bed and said,

"Look, tell us where that time bomb is." I never would think of a time bomb, but I could hear the ticking of somebody's watch and thought this was the time bomb . . . and then it felt like we were sitting in a restaurant together. At first he was sitting on the bed and the next picture was we were sitting in a restaurant together in a room or cubicle off to the side . . . and my friends were sitting around having dinner and the doctor said, "There are too many people here who are going to get hurt. We have to know where the bomb is!" And then that passed on and after a while I woke up and my nurse said, "You said some of the wildest things when you were asleep. . . ." Well, I hardly go to a restaurant, so I don't know why that happened to me. I have a watch which ticks and so that must be where the time bomb business came from.[20]

This man's postoperative delusion is clearly different from an NDE. He had grossly misperceived the meaning of certain objects and events in his immediate environment (i.e., the watch and the doctor) and had built these perceptions into the delusion that a "time bomb" was nearby. The NDE, on the other hand, is characterized by a clarity of thought and "visual" perception.

Another man made an interesting comparison between an illness-induced hallucination and an NDE. During the hallucinatory encounter, his perceptions assumed the "not me" quality of a spectator, while during a subsequent NDE, he clearly had felt that the essential "me" had left his physical body:

I was in a coma for seven or eight days and I had all those other convulsions. I had hallucinations then but they weren't the same. They were real—that is, they weren't like a dream, yet they weren't the same as I felt in that ambulance, in that in the hallucinations I'd be more like a spectator but in this experience [NDE] where I lifted out of my body, it was *me!* (I–53)

A similar contrast between an hallucinatory experience, this time from an intravenous narcotic, and an NDE was made by the following man:

S: [After receiving an intravenous narcotic in the emergency room for a severe headache, he was] driving home. Now, nobody warned me about this thing, but as I looked down the road, the perspective of the road wasn't as it gradually disappeared. The road went on and on and on. And it didn't follow the natural curves of the earth. And I could see little details way down there. I could tell you whether it was an ash or an elm tree 350 yards down the road. I could tell you from the shape of the leaf. I could see that good. I could look at this bedspread here [in hospital during interview] and you can see that it has little stitches and apertures between the stitch. I could look and tell you every fiber of the cloth that was woven together. I could see every one individually. I could look at your shirt from over here and I could see every aperture, every pore in your shirt. I could see it.

A: Was this similar to your experience when you had your cardiac arrest?

S: Similar but not anything like it. . . . I knew I was hallucinating [after receiving the drug for the headache]. I mean, I was perfectly aware of this. At the same time, I thought that it was not unpleasant and it's going to go away after a while, so just bear up under it and it will go away and your headache will be gone too. So I put up with it.

A: Was it frightening?

S: Well, yeah, I was afraid I might do something under the influence of it. If I was hallucinating that badly, I could easily trick myself into believing something was perfectly safe to do when it wouldn't be. I had common sense enough to know that was a no-no.

A: When you had the cardiac arrest, do you think you were hallucinating then?

S: No, sir. I surely wasn't. That was real. . . . I've lived with this thing for three years now and I haven't told anyone because I don't want them putting the straitjacket on me. . . . It's real as hell. (I-19)

Brief mention should also be made of the possibility that medications used during a near-death crisis event may actually *inhibit* the formation and/or later recollection of an NDE. Anecdotal support for this possibility was offered by a woman who had had an autoscopic NDE during a grand mal seizure from toxemia of pregnancy. As she "watched" her convulsing body in clear detail, her doctor administered a "shot" (probably phenobarbital) which seemingly interfered with the clarity of her "visual" perceptions:

Well, before they had given me the shot, I could see everything that was going on and it was very sharp in detail. . . . But after they gave

me the shot, it was almost a depressing feeling. I couldn't see everything as well as at first. It was like the clarity was gone from the
picture. I couldn't hear things as well. It was just getting darker
and it was like I was fading away. . . . I went to sleep and woke up
the next morning. (I–28)

In sum, the hallucinations and delusions reported by persons during
extreme illness or after the administration of medicinal narcotics differ
significantly from the NDE in both content and structure. Moreover, we
have clear documentation of many cases in which the NDE occurred in
the absence of any medicinal hallucinatory agent, thus making the drug-
induction hypothesis completely untenable in such situations.

Endorphin Release

> . . . a substance is elaborated in the brain which mimics morphine, to
> the extent that it is selectively bound to the same cellular receptors
> which appear to be specific for the attachment of morphine . . . an
> overabundant elaboration of a substance of this kind within the brain
> might itself be involved in the launching of death, either at death's
> appointed hour or, inappropriately, earlier on. Either way, it would
> ensure that the act of dying would be, by the nature of things, a
> painless and conceivably pleasant experience.[21]
>   Lewis Thomas, M.D.
>   President, Sloan-Kettering Cancer Institute
>   New York

Recently, a new substance was discovered within the human brain:
B-endorphin. This substance appears to possess many of the characteristics of morphine sulfate and may explain why some persons report having little or no pain following overwhelming trauma. It is not surprising,
then, that B-endorphins have been proposed as a cause of the profound
painlessness reported by persons during an NDE. A few studies have
been published which allow a comparison between the effects seen with
B-endorphin and the NDE.

A "Preliminary Communication" in the January 19, 1980, issue of
The Lancet, the English medical journal,[22] reported upon the injection of
B-endorphin directly into the cerebrospinal fluid of fourteen volunteer
patients with intractable pain associated with disseminated cancer. All
fourteen patients reported complete relief of pain. In twelve of these
cases, relief was evident within one to five minutes following the injection. However, total relief of pain lasted from 22 to 73 hours, a finding
at variance with reports of the NDE, where painlessness occurs only

during the NDE itself. As soon as the experience ends, physical pain abruptly returns. One man described his perception of pain during and following an autoscopic NDE with the following words:

> [During the NDE] It was nice. It didn't hurt. In fact, no feeling at all whatsoever. I could see but I couldn't feel. . . . I could see everything there. . . . The nurse was on this side of the bed with that machine. She picked up them shocker things and put one there and one right there [pointed to appropriate places on chest] and I seen my body flop like that and I was back. . . . [After regaining consciousness] It hurt! . . . It burned. Burned all the hair off my chest, with a blister here and here. . . . I told her [the nurse] don't do that no more. (I-63-2)

Another man put it this way:

> I was hurting real bad. . . . But all of a sudden the pain completely stopped and I could feel my being rising out of my body. It seemed like I got up to ceiling high and I could look back and see my body and I looked dead. I could see the attendant working on me. . . . Then I started floating back down to my body. As soon as I got down to my body, the pain came back. Tremendous pain. (I-53)

If the painless state entered into during the NDE was due to a massive cerebral release of B-endorphin, then the painlessness should be expected to persist much longer than the seconds to minutes typical of the experience.

Second, in the majority of patients injected with B-endorphin, somnolence and sleep were reported to be the major psychodynamic effects of the substance. This observation does not fit with the state of "hyperalertness" described during the NDE, in which there is a clarity of "vision" and thought.

Finally, it was noted in the fourteen patients injected with B-endorphin that "During the period of pain relief, perception of venipuncture and light touch remained intact."[23] Again, this finding differs from the NDE, in which a *total* absence of pain and discomfort was described. In fact, one woman made the following remark regarding when she was "out of body" and "watching" her physician probe her wrist with a venipuncture needle: "I can remember I couldn't feel when they were probing to put the needle in. That was unusual because you can usually feel that. . . . This is the first time I can honestly say an IV didn't hurt me." (I-45-2)

Based on our present knowledge of B-endorphin, it appears unlikely that this substance can account for the NDE.

Temporal Lobe Seizure

These experiences such as reported by Moody are nothing more than temporal lobe seizures. I see several patients a week who describe similar experiences during their seizure episodes. Wilder Penfield described these phenomena in the early 1950's using electrostimulation techniques of the brain. That was before he, like Moody, got caught up in the religious overtones of these occurrences. Penfield made some very significant contributions to neurology up to that point.[24]

A professor of neurology

Epileptogenic discharges originating in the parietal or temporal lobes (nonmotor portions) of the brain may produce a complex set of phenomena known as a psychical seizure. These seizures have been extensively investigated by Dr. Wilder Penfield at the Montreal Neurological Institute. Using neurosurgical techniques developed through years of operative experience, Penfield explored the subjective elements of the psychical seizure by electrically stimulating different regions of the temporal and parietal lobes in partially exposed brains of conscious human patients. During these artificially induced seizures, Penfield's patients reported the following:

1. Sensory illusions involving the interpretation of environmental events—distortion of size or location of nearby objects (visual illusions); distortion of source of intensity of sounds (auditory illusions); and feelings of detachment from self and environment (illusions of remoteness).

2. Feelings of fear, sadness or loneliness, without joy, happiness or other positive emotional states.

3. Visual and auditory hallucinations—perception of human-like figures of a "horrible and threatening nature"; strange music or voices; and "replays" of previous life experiences:

Complex visual and auditory hallucinations have occurred during stimulation of the superior and lateral surfaces of both temporal lobes. The electrical stimulation can call back a sequence of past experience. It is as though a wire recorder, or a strip of cinematographic film with sound track, had been set in motion within the brain. A previous experience—its sights and sounds and thoughts—seems to pass through the mind of the patient on the operating table. It comes back to him in great detail, with conscious awareness of the same things to which he paid attention in the actual experience. At the same time he is conscious of the present. He reexperiences some period from his past while still retaining his hold on the present. The recollection of the experiential sequence stops suddenly when the electric current ceases. But it can be activated with reapplication of the electric current.[25]

4. Forced thinking—the crowding of random thoughts and ideas into the mind of the patient in an automatic and obtrusive way.

In addition to these four characteristics of the psychical seizure, a variety of other sensations commonly occurred that originated in specific regions of the temporal or parietal cortex:

buzzing sound in Heschl's gyrus, odors in the uncus, alimentary tract sensations in the insula, tastes in the cortex just above the insula, somatic sensations from the "second sensory" area above the insula, and head sensations and body sensations in the deep portions of the temporal tip.[26]

When the psychical seizure is compared to the NDE with regard to these characteristics, several significant differences are apparent. (1) Perception of the immediate environment is often distorted in the psychical seizure and is undisturbed in the NDE. (2) The characteristic emotion during a seizure is fear, sadness and loneliness, whereas calm, peace and joy pervade the NDE. (3) The senses of smell and taste are characteristically present in many seizures but absent in the NDE. (4) The reliving of past life events involves a random, single event of no particular significance in the seizure but consists of multiple significant events experienced in rapid succession in an NDE. (5) Forced thinking is present during the seizure but absent during the NDE. Thus the classic description of the temporal lobe or psychical seizure by Dr. Penfield and others does not fit with the NDE.

Altered States of Consciousness

... all of the anecdotes about life after death/life can be explained phenomenologically as *altered states of consciousness.* There are three primary etiologies: (a) physiological—hypoxia, anoxia, hepatic delirium, uremia, Meduna's CO_2 therapy, etc.; (b) pharmacological—"mind benders," narcotics, steroids, pentylenetetrazol (Metrazol), insulin, barbiturates, and other psychotherapeutic medications; and (c) psychological—dissociative reaction, panic, psychosis, etc.[27]

Nathan Schnaper, M.D.
Professor of Psychiatry
University of Maryland

Dr. Arnold Ludwig, in an article entitled "Altered States of Consciousness" in the September 1966 issue of *Archives of General Psychiatry,* defined the term "altered state of consciousness" as

> any mental state(s), induced by various physiological, psychological, or pharmacologic maneuvers or agents, which can be recognized subjectively by the individual himself (or by an objective observer of the individual) as representing a sufficient deviation in subjective experience or psychological functioning from certain general norms for that individual during alert, waking consciousness.[28]

According to Ludwig, individuals experiencing an altered state of consciousness commonly report: (1) alterations in concentration, attention, memory or judgment; (2) disturbances in the sense of time; (3) fears of losing contact with reality; (4) emotional extremes ranging from joyous ecstasy to profound fears; (5) splitting of mind from body; (6) perceptual distortions; (7) profound truth and insight; (8) ineffability; (9) a renewed sense of hope; and (10) hypersuggestibility.

Using Dr. Ludwig's criteria, the NDE would easily fit into the overall category of altered states of consciousness as suggested by Dr. Schnaper in the quotation at the beginning of this section. The causes of altered states of consciousness are as numerous as its various manifestations briefly summarized by Dr. Ludwig. Many of these causes have already been examined in this chapter: the deliriums (hallucinations, dreams, etc.), the pharmacological causes (narcotics, endorphins, etc.) and the psychological considerations (depersonalization, prior expectations, subconscious fabrications, etc.). Yet to be discussed are hypoxia (inadequate oxygen level) and hypercarbia (elevated carbon dioxide level).

Brain *hypoxia* is a common physiological consequence of a near-death crisis event. Normally, an adequate supply of oxygen to the brain is ensured by its rich arterial blood supply. Interference with cerebral blood flow for only a brief period of time will result in a marked alteration of mental function. Total cessation of blood flow to the brain, as seen in a cardiac arrest, will produce unconsciousness in seconds and progressive brain damage in three to five minutes. Prior to unconsciousness, however, a series of subjective phenomena may be encountered by the person with an increasingly hypoxic brain. These phenomena may be collectively viewed as an altered state of consciousness resulting from progressive brain hypoxia.

In the 1920s, two physicians, Y. Henderson and H. W. Haggard, studied the mental and physiological effects of hypoxia by placing human volunteers in an air chamber and slowly lowering the concentration of oxygen.[29] They found that as the level of inspired oxygen was lowered the person's mental and physical abilities became progessively impaired until convulsions occurred and respiration ceased. No experiences resembling an NDE were reported.

In the 1930s, another physician, R. A. McFarland, conducted additional research on the effects of brain hypoxia. His observations were made on members of the International High Altitude Expedition to Chile. McFarland found that mountain climbers exposed to the hypoxic conditions found at extreme elevations reported greater effort being required to carry out tasks, mental laziness, sense of heightened irritability, difficulty in concentrating, slowness in reasoning, and difficulty in remembering.[30]

From these studies we see that as oxygen supply to the brain decreases, there is a progressive muddling and confusion of cognitive abilities. This is in sharp contrast to the clarity of mental functioning and awareness described by persons who have had an NDE. Moreover, the sequence of events characteristic of an NDE was not triggered by the progressive lowering of brain oxygen levels to the point of unconsciousness. Thus brain hypoxia per se cannot account for the typical manifestations of an NDE.

Hypercarbia, or elevated levels of carbon dioxide (CO_2) in the brain, may also produce an altered state of consciousness. Carbon dioxide is normally formed in the brain as the end product of brain cell metabolism. The rich blood supply that carries oxygen to the brain is also responsible for transporting CO_2 out of the brain, to be expelled in the lungs. Cessation of this blood flow, as happens with a cardiac arrest, will rapidly result in a hypercarbic brain.

L. J. Meduna, a University of Illinois psychiatrist in the 1950s, studied the effects of varying degrees of hypercarbia in the hope that carbon dioxide treatment would prove helpful for psychoneurotic conditions. To 150 psychoneurotic patients and 50 normal people serving as controls, he administered, by mask, a variable number of inhalations of a gaseous mixture containing 30 percent CO_2 and 70 percent O_2 (room air contains 0 percent CO_2, 21 percent O_2).

During these CO_2 treatments, Meduna's subjects described a wide variety of subjective sensory phenomena. Some of these experiences strongly resembled the NDE, and included the perception of a bright light, a sense of bodily detachment, revival of past memories, ineffability, telepathic communion with a religious presence, and feelings of cosmic importance and ecstasy. For example:

I felt as though I was looking down at myself, as though I was way out here in space. . . . I felt sort of separated.

It was a wonderful feeling. It was marvelous. I felt very light and I didn't know where I was. . . . And then I thought that something was happening to me. This wasn't night. I wasn't dreaming. . . . And then I felt a wonderful feeling as if I was out in space.

I felt myself being separated; my soul drawing apart from the physical being, was drawn upward seemingly to leave the earth and to go upward where it reached a greater Spirit with Whom there was a communion, producing a remarkable, new relaxation and deep security.[31]

Other elements of the hypercarbic experience, however, were not associated with the NDE: perception of brightly colored complex geometric figures or patterns ("stained-glass window effects"); animation of fantasized objects (musical notes floating by); compulsions to solve mathematical puzzles or enigmas; polyopic vision (seeing in duplicate, triplicate, etc.); and frightening perceptions of "shapeless and objectless horror."

Despite these differences, the strong resemblances suggest a possible association between some of these events. Could the buildup of CO_2 in the brain be the trigger that initiates the NDE? Perhaps so. However, many of Meduna's subjects exposed to ninety or more inhalations of the CO_2 mixture also demonstrated signs of extreme neurological dysfunction:

the pupils became rigid, the eyes roll upward, and opisthotonus, tonic extension of extremities, and areflexia ensue. These tonic seizures, which last from 30 to 90 seconds after removal of the mask, are followed by stupor for one to two minutes and are typical of decerebrate seizures.[32]

This physiologic description of the effects of extremely high CO_2 levels in the brain resembles in many ways a clinical report of a patient during a cardiac arrest or other near-death crisis events.* Moreover, the subjectively reported experiences of the hypercarbic subject and the near-death victim are also, in part, similar. Regarding the experiences of his hypercarbic subjects, Dr. Meduna had this to say:

During the CO_2 treatment, brains of different persons—persons with divergent emotional needs—produce similar or even identical phenomena. These phenomena, moreover, are not specific of the function of the agent. . . . The imperceptible transition from "real" dreams to the CO_2-produced sensory phenomena suggests the same conclusions:

* No serious side effects were reported by Meduna in subjects receiving CO_2 treatments, however.

1. All the phenomena—dreams, hallucinations, eidetic imagery—rests on some underlying physiological function of some brain structures, which function operates independently from what, in psychiatry, is called personality.

2. These phenomena are only superficially invaded and modified by psychological problems and troubles of the individual.[33]

Thus, despite the wide variety of patients, with "divergent emotional needs," Dr. Meduna identified a common thread in their experiences when exposed to extreme hypercarbic conditions. He chose to identify this common thread as "some underlying physiological function of some brain structures" which operates independent of the "personality" and the "problems and troubles of the individual." Meduna's observation is quite similar to my findings with the NDE: that it appears to be a natural phenomenological process which can be entered into and modified in certain individual ways, but which maintains a basic structure independent of the whims and fantasies present in the subconscious minds of various individuals. However, the question still remains: Were these experiences which were reported by Meduna's patients and which resembled the NDE caused by the high levels of carbon dioxide per se or were they due to some other mechanism associated with the patient's CO_2-induced near-death condition?

In this regard, I found one man in my study who actually had his blood oxygen and carbon dioxide levels measured *at the time of his NDE* and cardiac arrest (see page 104). While physically unconscious during this autoscopic NDE, he clearly "observed" a doctor inserting a needle into his groin to obtain blood from his femoral artery for a blood gas analysis. The results from the laboratory later indicated that his arterial oxygen level was well *above* normal (this is frequently the case when high concentrations of oxygen are administered to a patient during cardiopulmonary resuscitation) and his arterial carbon dioxide level was actually *lower* than normal (actual values were: $pO_2 = 138$, $pCO_2 = 28$, pH $= 7.46$). The fact that he had "visually" observed this blood gas procedure indicates that the blood was obtained at the time his experience was occurring. Thus, in this one documented case, neither a low oxygen level (hypoxia) nor a high carbon dioxide level (hypercarbia) was present to explain the NDE!

11

Thoughts on the Meaning of the Near-Death Experience

AT THE BEGINNING of the preceding chapter I referred to an article written by Dr. Richard S. Blacher in the November 23, 1979, issue of the *Journal of the American Medical Association,* in which Dr. Blacher suggested that the NDE was a "fantasy of death" and warned "the physician must be especially wary of accepting religious belief as scientific data." My response to Dr. Blacher's article, published several months later, ended with the plea that "equal caution should be exercised in accepting scientific belief as scientific data" when considering the NDE. The reason I gave for this plea was that none of the proposed medical or scientific explanations for the NDE could fully account for the NDE. Dr. Blacher published a rebuttal to my remarks, which began as follows:

> Dr. Sabom takes me to task for describing the episodes [i.e., NDEs] as "fantasy." By using this word, I locate the phenomenon within the patient's psyche. . . . The alternative to the intrapsychic location would be one of something (the soul?) leaving the person in reality and hovering over the table. I do not think one has to apologize for scientific belief if one does not accept the ideas of spirits wandering around the emergency room.[1]

I agree: one should not have to apologize for a scientific belief that does not accept an idea yet to be confirmed by objective techniques of observation and analysis. I began this study of NDEs with the firm conviction that the scientific method of investigation is the best approach for advancing our knowledge of natural phenomena, and I continue to support this view. But to say that an idea has not yet been accepted in a scientific sense does not mean that such an idea should not at least be scientifically considered as a possible explanation for an unexplained phenomenon. For it is the premise of objective neutrality which has made the scientific method such a useful investigative process: all available hypotheses must be carefully examined before a conclusion can be reached.

Returning, now, to the firsthand descriptive accounts of the NDE itself, we find typical the following remarks:

From a 45-year-old college graduate who admits to infrequent church attendance: "The only thing I saw was my body lying on the bed. I keep insisting to everybody that the spirit left the body and that's all there is to it." (I–60)

From a 48-year-old high school graduate who attends church on a weekly basis: "But all of a sudden the pain completely stopped and I could feel *my being* rising out of my body. It seemed like I got up to about ceiling high and I could look back and see my body and I looked dead." (I–53)

From a 50-year-old college graduate with weekly church attendance: "With the cardiac arrest [and NDE], *I* was looking down from the ceiling and there were no ifs, ands or buts about it." (I–14)

From a 46-year-old high school graduate who rarely attends church: "It seemed like I was apart. . . . It seemed like I was up here [on the ceiling] and it [the cardioversion] grabbed *me* and *my body* and forced it back, pushed it back. . . . I *know* it was real. I *know* that I was up there. I could swear on a Bible that I was there. . . . I can't prove it to none of those people there because they didn't see me. There's no way you can prove it, but I was there!" (I–63–2)

We have examined these near-death accounts from the standpoint of conventional scientific thought, which holds that the NDE is some form of mental elaboration (i.e., a dream, hallucination or fantasy) that is conjured up in the mind of a dying individual and gives the false impression that perceptions are occurring out of the body. With this approach, however, all elements of the NDE cannot be adequately accounted for. In the spirit of objective neutrality, let us now consider the NDE using a second approach, which makes no a priori assumptions about the nature of the experience: Could the NDE actually be occurring precisely as described—*out of the body?*

But how can we consider, in a scientific sense, the possibility that the NDE is "something (the soul?) leaving the person in reality and hovering over the table"? Western scientific thought is firmly molded around the premise that all aspects of human consciousness—our "total being"—can be or eventually will be explained through the physiologic interaction of the cellular components of the human brain. In other words, human experience is exclusively an "intrapsychic" event. To entertain the possibility that some presently undefined portion of the human organism can split apart from the anatomic brain and perceive reality from an out-of-body location (i.e., "extrapsychic" perception) violates this traditional basic premise. But is this premise a scientific "fact" or a preconceived notion based on theories and hypotheses yet to be substantiated in the scientific arena?

Unfortunately, a major problem with scientific method is that facts taken to be inviolable statements of truth are, in reality, only *theoretical* entities which have been awarded factual status within a particular conceptual framework. Furthermore, as one professor of psychology has put it so well, one "can only attribute factual status to an observation if a theory is available to determine that it is indeed significant, i.e. a fact. Facts are theoretically significant observations, not neutral or 'hard' data."[2]

Thus, to consider the NDE as a possible manifestation of an "out-of-body" experience, we must first establish a "theoretical (or conceptual) framework" within which this explanation can be viewed as a "significant" possibility. Such a theoretical framework would need to allow the following question to be raised: Is out-of-body perception indeed occurring during the NDE, and if so, is some element of the human organism (the *mind?*) separating from the physical determinants of consciousness (the *brain?*) to accomplish such a feat?

This type of framework—that is, one that allows for the possibility that our being may consist of two fundamental elements, a "mind" and a "brain"—was considered to be a legitimate proposition by Sir Charles Sherrington, a Nobel laureate in medicine in the 1930s. In his words:

> We have to regard the relation of mind to brain as not merely unsolved, but still devoid of a basis for its very beginning . . . that our being should consist of two fundamental elements [mind and brain] offers, I suppose, no greater inherent improbability than that it should rest on one only [brain].[3]

Sherrington's beliefs in a dualistic system of mind *and* brain were extended by another physician, Wilder Penfield, through a lifetime of neurosurgical research into the structure and function of the human brain. Early in his career in the 1930s, Penfield challenged one of the prevailing concepts of his time: that the highest brain function (i.e., the control of consciousness) was located in the massive convolutions of the cerebral cortex. He noted that large sections of the cerebral cortex could be surgically removed without abolishing consciousness. However, interference or injury to the small area of the higher brain stem known as the diencephalon resulted in unconsciousness. The diencephalon, thought Penfield, was the seat of the "highest brain mechanism," which controlled the state of consciousness.

Through years of clinical and neurosurgical research with epileptic patients, Penfield elaborated on this concept of the "highest brain mechanism." Portions of the cerebral cortexes of epileptics were surgically exposed by Penfield in order to isolate and to treat the focus of the seizure disturbance, using electrostimulation techniques specifically designed for this purpose. In addition to offering new hope to patients suffering from intractable epileptic seizures, Penfield "mapped" the different anatomical areas of the brain in intricate detail. From this work, he postulated that the anatomic brain was in reality two separate but related units. One unit, termed the "computer mechanism," was located in the parietal lobes and served the sensory and motor functions of the brain. The other unit, the "mind mechanism," encompassed the interpretative abilities of the brain and was seated in the frontal and temporal lobes. The centers for both units were separately represented in the diencephalon—the "highest brain mechanism." Using this framework, Penfield could account for the varied manifestations of his patients' seizure disorders.

For instance, a seizure focus located in the parietal cortex, or "computer mechanism," would primarily result in uncontrolled stimulation of the sensory and motor functions of the brain, leading to jerking movements of the arms and legs (grand mal seizure). On the other hand, Penfield found that a seizure focus in the frontal or temporal cortex, or "mind mechanism," would inactivate the interpretative abilities of the brain and create an "automaton," or "one who has lost his mind." In such an attack,

> the patient becomes suddenly unconscious, but, since other mechanisms in the brain continue to function, he changes into an automaton. He may wander about, confused and aimless. Or he may continue to carry out

whatever purpose his mind was in the act of handing on to his automatic sensory-motor mechanism when the highest brain mechanism went out of action. Or he follows a stereotyped, habitual pattern of behavior. In every case, the automaton can make few, if any, decisions for which there has been no precedent . . . he will have complete amnesia for the period. . . . [The automaton is] a thing without that indefinable attribute, a sense of humor. The automaton is incapable of thrilling to the beauty of a sunset or of experiencing contentment, happiness, love, compassion. These, like all awarenesses, are functions of the mind.[4]

Shortly before his death in the mid-1970s, Penfield reflected on the accomplishments of his neurosurgical career in a book entitled *The Mystery of the Mind*. In it, he describes his failed attempts to account for both the "computer" and the "mind" mechanisms of the human brain using elaborate anatomical and physiological theories. In what he termed a "final examination of the evidence," Penfield concluded that:

For myself, after a professional lifetime spent in trying to discover how the brain accounts for the mind, it comes as a surprise now to discover, during this final examination of the evidence, that the dualist hypothesis [separation of mind and brain] seems the more reasonable of the two possible explanations. . . . Mind comes into action and goes out of action with the highest brain-mechanism, it is true. But the mind has energy. The form of that energy is different from that of neuronal potentials that travel the axone pathways. There I must leave it.[5]

Recent investigation into the techniques of biofeedback has shown that in a laboratory setting, a human subject can modify certain bodily functions heretofore regarded as not under voluntary control. Through specific cues and methods of reinforcement, these individuals can be "trained" to control their own blood pressure, body temperature and pain thresholds, and even their brain wave activity. If the workings of the cellular components of the highest brain levels can be controlled through voluntary effort, then what and where is the source of this volitional control?

Certainly we have a long way to go before this question and others about the human brain can be answered. But these theories proposed by Sherrington, Penfield and others at least establish a framework in which to consider the NDE as a possible "out-of-body" event: a *mind-brain split*. If the human brain is actually composed of two fundamental elements—the "mind" and the "brain"—then could the near-death crisis event somehow trigger a transient splitting of the mind from the brain in many individuals? Could the "separated self" in the NDE represent the detached "mind," which, according to Penfield, is capable of experiencing contentment, happiness, love, compassion and awareness, while the unconscious physical body represents the remains of the "computer"—a lifeless automaton? The descriptions of the NDE given by individuals with varying backgrounds and beliefs suggest such an occurrence: "the *spirit* left the body" (I–60); "I could feel *my being* rising out of my body" (I–53); "[the cardioversion] grabbed *me* and *my body* and forced it back" (I–63–2). But does the *content* of these NDEs fit with the notion of an out-of-body experience or a mind-brain split?

During the *autoscopic* portion of the NDE, near-death survivors claimed to have seen and heard events in the vicinity of their own unconscious physical bodies from a detached elevated position. The details of these perceptions were found to be accurate in all instances where corroborating evidence was available. Moreover, there appeared to be no plausible explanation for the accuracy of these observations involving the usual physical senses. An out-of-body (extrasensory?) mechanism would explain both the personal interpretation afforded these experiences by those who had them (i.e., "the spirit left the body") and the "visual" accuracy of the autoscopic observations.

My own beliefs on this matter are leaning in this direction. The out-of-body hypothesis simply seems to fit best with the data at hand. I am well aware, however, that my current beliefs are based on the analysis of only a small number of autoscopic NDEs. Much additional research is needed, and is presently under way in many centers.* I am also aware that my arguments against the more traditional NDE explanations in earlier portions of this book do not ipso facto prove that the out-of-body proposal is correct. Certainly other explanations for the autoscopic NDE—explanations I have not addressed—may eventually account for all these findings. I do believe, however, that the observations in this book concerning the autoscopic NDE indicate that this experience cannot be casually dismissed as some mental fabrication, and that serious

---

* Dr. Kenneth Ring, a professor of psychology at the University of Connecticut, is currently investigating the NDE and has recently published many of his findings in a book entitled *Life at Death: A Scientific Investigation of the Near Death Experience*. Another study is being conducted by John Audette and several physicians in East Peoria, Illinois. The NDE is also being investigated at the University of Michigan (Bruce Greyson, M.D.), the University of Iowa (Russell Noyes, M.D.), the University of Virginia (Ian Stevenson, M.D.), Western New Mexico University (Craig Lundahl, Ph.D.), the University of California at Berkeley (Charles Garfield, Ph.D.), Seattle Pacific University (Annalee Oakes, R.N., M.A., C.C.R.N.), and in Denver, Colorado (Fred Schoonmaker, M.D.). Moreover, an international forum for the exchange of research findings and ideas concerning the NDE has recently been established—The International Association for Near-Death Studies, U–20, University of Connecticut, Storrs, Connecticut 06268.

scientific consideration must be given to alternative, perhaps less traditional, explanations.

What if the autoscopic NDE *does* turn out to be a true out-of-body experience resulting from some sort of mind-brain split? Questions will still remain as to *how* and *why* this should occur at the point of death. My guess is that the autoscopic event is initiated by some type of trigger, neurochemical or otherwise, which is touched off at a particular point in the dying process. This trigger, however, is apparently not limited to the near-death situation, since autoscopic-type experiences have been reported under a variety of other circumstances—i.e., during general anesthesia (see Chapter 6) and during non-near-death moments in the lives of persons who have previously had a true NDE (see Chapter 8).

But what can be said of the *transcendental* NDE? I know of no way to corroborate the details reported in these experiences, as has been done with the autoscopic NDE. However, there is a consistency to these reports which would not be expected from individual mental fabrications. Moreover, in the combined NDE, the transcendental portion occurs in sequence following the autoscopic elements and is perceived by the person as being equally vivid and real as its autoscopic forerunner. This recalls Negovskii's definition of clinical death (page 8) in which he refers to the transition from clinical to biological death as being "simultaneously a break and a continuous process."[6] If the NDE is but the experiential counterpart of the physiologic transition to biological death, the autoscopic and transcendental elements of the NDE may be all pieces of the same puzzle. Which pieces of this puzzle (i.e., the autoscopic, transcendental or combined NDE), if any, appear at the point of near-death is almost certainly determined by the interplay of countless factors which have yet to be discovered.

Does the NDE represent a glimpse of an afterlife, of life after death? As a physician and scientist, I cannot, of course, say for sure that the NDE is indicative of what is to come at the moment of *final* bodily death. These experiences were encountered during waning moments of life. Those reporting these experiences were *not brought back from the dead,* but were rescued from a point *very close to death.* Thus, in the strictest sense, these experiences are encounters of *near*-death, and not of death itself. Since I suspect that the NDE is a reflection of a mind-brain split, I cannot help but wonder why such an event should occur at the point of near-death. Could the mind which splits apart from the physical brain be, in essence, the "soul," which continues to exist after final bodily death, according to some religious doctrines?

As I see it, this is the ultimate question that has been raised by reports of the NDE. It is here, at the point of near-death, that scientific facts and theories interface with religious doctrines and speculations. In my own life, I have been deeply touched by the testimonies of those whose stories fill this book. As a physician, I have evaluated the medical circumstances that have surrounded these experiences and have been utterly amazed at the survival of many of these people whose physical condition plainly seemed to rule against their continuing to live. I have been equally fascinated by the descriptions of their journeys while unconscious and near death. My personal reaction to these events is not so much a "scientifically weighed" response as it is a keenly felt identification with the tears of joy and sorrow that have accompanied the unfolding of many of these stories. In short, my involvement in the lives and deaths of the people in this book has made me humble to the ways of the universe, much like Albert Einstein, who once wrote:

> Everyone who is seriously involved in the pursuit of science becomes convinced that a Spirit is manifest in the Laws of the Universe—a Spirit vastly superior to that of man, and one in the face of which we, with our modest powers, must feel humble.[7]

For it is precisely this "Spirit" which has been acknowledged time and time again by the majority of those encountering an NDE:

> Dr. Sabom, I think it's God's work. That's the only thing I can figure. God had me that time and he could have kept me. From this experience, I know there is a life after death and not just death itself. (I–67)

> I think once you've penetrated the big secret just a bit like I did, it's enough to convince you, enough to convince me that I'm going to have no fear. . . . I don't think God wanted me to die . . . if he wanted me, he would have kept me. . . . He wanted me to get a peek into this big secret and shove me right back again. (I–23)

And it is precisely this "Spirit" which seems to live on in the lives of those who were touched by some ineffable truth encountered face to face at death's closest moments.

> For now we see through a glass, darkly; but then face to face: now I know in part; but then shall I know even as also I am known.
>
> I Cor. 13:12

Appendix

Explanation of Statistical Methods

THROUGHOUT THIS APPENDIX, a statistical value of probability—the "p value"—is used to compare possible differences in specific observations made between two groups of people. Consider, for example, the hypothetical proposition that drug A is helpful in preventing death in persons with disease X. To test this proposition in a group of 100 persons with disease X, drug A is given to 50 persons with the disease and no treatment is given to the remaining 50. Thirty of the 50 persons treated with drug A die, whereas *all* 50 of the nontreated persons die. Using statistical methods of analysis, the results of treating persons with drug A can be compared with the results of nontreatment to determine if drug A is indeed helpful in a statistical sense in preventing death in persons with disease X. Moreover, using the statistical analysis of the drug treatment results, we can determine the percent probability of being *wrong* in stating that drug A is helpful in preventing death from disease X. If this percent probability of being wrong is computed to be 5 percent or *below*, then the conclusion that drug A is helpful in preventing death from disease X is said to have reached a "significant" level of probability. The smaller the probability of being wrong (i.e., the less the "p value"), the more confident we can be in stating that the statistical conclusion is correct. "P values" are presented in decimals: 5 percent being .05, 2 percent being .02, 1 percent being .01, etc. Thus "p values" below 5 percent (i.e., p $<$.05) indicate that the difference observed between two groups of people (in this instance, the difference between the treatment and nontreatment of disease X with drug A) is, by convention, a "significant" difference. In this hypothetical case involving drug A and disease X, the "p value" calculates to be less than .1 percent (p $<$.001)—a highly significant difference. The methods used to determine the "p value" in this book are the student's t-test and the chi-squared test.

TABLE I: BACKGROUND CHARACTERISTICS OF INTERVIEWEES

Interview Number[1]	Type of Interview[2]	Age	Sex	Race	Residence[3]	Years of Education	Occupation[4]	Religion[5]	Frequency of Church Attendance[6]	Previous Knowledge of NDE
1	P	32	M	W	B/Fla.	17	Cler-Sales	Prot.	2	No
2	P	54	M	W	B/Fla.	9	Lab-Serv	Prot.	2	Yes
3	P	51	M	W	C/Fla.	15	Cler-Sales	Prot.	3	No
4	P	32	M	W	B/Fla.	12	Lab-Serv	Agnos.	0	No
5	P	57	M	W	B/Ga.	15	Lab-Serv	Agnos.	0	No
6	P	32	F	W	D/Fla.	12	Cler-Sales	Prot.	1	No
7	P	65	M	W	B/Ga.	12	Cler-Sales	Prot.	2	No
8	P	56	M	W	C/Fla.	16	Prof	Cath.	2	No
9	P	60	F	W	D/Fla.	19	Prof	Jew	1	No
10	P	51	M	W	C/Ind.	7	Lab-Serv	Prot.	2	Yes
11	P	60	M	W	B/Fla.	14	Cler-Sales	Prot.	1	Yes
12	P	75	M	W	C/Fla.	10	Lab-Serv	Prot.	4	No
13	P	66	M	W	B/Fla.	12	Cler-Sales	Prot.	3	No
14	P	50	M	W	B/Fla.	16	Prof	Cath.	4	No
15	P	35	M	W	B/Ga.	14	Lab-Serv	Prot.	4	No
16	P	40	F	W	B/Fla.	12	Lab-Serv	Prot.	1	No

[1] *Interview Number:* "s" denotes surgical case.

[2] *Type of Interview:* P = Prospective; R = Referred.

[3] *Residence:* Numerator—A = rural; B = township of < 10,000; C = city of 10,000 to 100,000; D = urban center of > 100,000 population; Denominator—abbreviation for state.

[4] *Occupation:* Lab-Serv = laborer-services; Cler-Sales = clerical-sales; Prof = professional.

[5] *Religion:* Prot. = Protestant; Cath. = Catholic; Agnos. = Agnostic.

[6] *Frequency of Church Attendance:* 0 = agnostic; 1 = none; 2 = less than monthly; 3 = 1 to 3 times per month; 4 = weekly.

TABLE I: (cont'd)

Interview Number	Type of Interview	Age	Sex	Race	Residence	Years of Education	Occupation	Religion	Frequency of Church Attendance	Previous Knowledge of NDE
17	P	39	F	W	B/Fla.	10	Lab-Serv	Prot.	1	Yes
18	P	32	F	W	B/Fla.	13	Lab-Serv	Prot.	4	No
19	P	52	M	W	A/Fla.	16	Cler-Sales	Agnos.	0	No
20	P	38	M	W	A/Fla.	12	Lab-Serv	Prot.	1	No
21	P	58	M	W	B/Fla.	12	Lab-Serv	Prot.	2	No
22	P	44	M	W	B/Fla.	10	Lab-Serv	Prot.	4	No
23	P	60	M	W	C/Fla.	12	Lab-Serv	Cath.	2	No
24	P	58	M	W	B/Fla.	12	Cler-Sales	Prot.	3	No
25	P	60	M	W	C/Fla.	5	Lab-Serv	Prot.	1	No
26	P	58	M	W	B/Fla.	12	Lab-Serv	Cath.	3	No
27	P	69	M	W	A/Fla.	8	Cler-Sales	Prot.	4	No
28	P	37	F	W	C/Fla.	12	Lab-Serv	Agnos.	0	No
29	P	23	F	W	B/Fla.	14	Prof	Prot.	2	No
30	P	42	M	W	B/Fla.	9	Lab-Serv	Prot.	2	No
31	P	56	M	W	B/Fla.	6	Lab-Serv	Prot.	4	No
32	P	44	M	W	B/Fla.	16	Prof	Agnos.	0	No
33	P	47	M	W	B/Fla.	12	Cler-Sales	Prot.	3	No
34	R	67	F	W	D/Fla.	12	Lab-Serv	Prot.	4	No
35	R	75	F	W	D/Ala.	13	Lab-Serv	Cath.	4	No
36	R	62	F	W	C/Wisc.	12	Lab-Serv	Prot.	2	No
37	R	55	F	W	C/Fla.	16	Prof	Cath.	3	No
38	R	49	M	W	D/Fla.	16	Cler-Sales	Prot.	1	No
39s	R	62	F	W	C/Pa.	12	Lab-Serv	Cath.	4	No
40s	R	42	F	W	D/NY	12	Cler-Sales	Cath.	4	No

41	R	55	F	W	C/Fla.	10	Cler-Sales	Prot.	4	No
42	R	50	M	W	C/N.C.	18	Prof	Prot.	3	No
43	R	60	F	W	C/Fla.	12	Lab-Serv	Prot.	3	No
44	R	43	M	W	C/N.J.	12	Cler-Sales	Cath.	2	Yes
45	R	60	F	W	C/Ohio	12	Lab-Serv	Prot.	1	No
46	R	84	F	W	B/Ill.	16	Prof	Prot.	4	No
47	R	63	M	W	C/Fla.	12	Prof	Prot.	1	No
48s	R	52	F	W	B/Fla.	12	Cler-Sales	Prot.	4	Yes
49	R	62	M	W	D/Fla.	20	Prof	Prot.	4	No
50s	R	55	F	W	C/Mich.	12	Prof	Cath.	3	No
51s	R	62	F	W	C/Fla.	16	Lab-Serv	Prot.	4	No
52	R	54	M	W	C/Ill.	14	Cler-Sales	Prot.	4	No
53	R	48	M	W	D/Fla.	12	Cler-Sales	Prot.	4	No
54	R	73	F	W	C/Fla.	19	Prof	Prot.	1	No
55s	R	60	M	W	C/Tex.	12	Cler-Sales	Prot.	3	No
56	R	53	M	W	A/Fla.	11	Cler-Sales	Prot.	4	No
57	R	60	M	W	C/Mich.	10	Lab-Serv	Cath.	1	No
58s	R	56	F	W	B/Md.	18	Cler-Sales	Prot.	2	No
59s	R	58	F	W	C/Fla.	14	Cler-Sales	Prot.	2	No
60	R	45	M	W	B/Ga.	16	Prof	Prot.	2	No
61	R	50	M	W	C/Pa.	12	Lab-Serv	Prot.	3	No
62	R	58	F	W	D/Fla.	16	Lab-Serv	Prot.	3	No
63	R	46	M	W	B/Ga.	12	Lab-Serv	Prot.	2	No
64	R	24	F	W	C/Fla.	16	Prof	Agnos.	0	No
65	R	54	M	W	D/Ga.	12	Lab-Serv	Prot.	4	No
66	R	55	M	W	D/Ga.	9	Lab-Serv	Prot.	1	No
67	R	62	M	B	B/Fla.	8	Lab-Serv	Prot.	3	No
68	R	33	M	W	D/Ga.	12	Cler-Sales	Prot.	2	No
69	R	35	M	B	D/Ga.	19	Prof	Prot.	1	No
70s	R	41	F	W	C/Mo.	16	Cler-Sales	Cath.	1	No

192

TABLE I: (cont'd)

Interview Number	Type of Interview	Age	Sex	Race	Residence	Years of Education	Occupation	Religion	Frequency of Church Attendance	Previous Knowledge of NDE
71s	P	48	M	W	D/Ga.	18	Prof	Prot.	4	No
72	P	57	M	W	B/Fla.	12	Lab-Serv	Agnos.	0	No
73	P	46	M	W	C/Fla.	17	Prof	Prot.	1	Yes
74	P	67	M	W	B/Fla.	12	Lab-Serv	Prot.	3	Yes
75	P	51	M	W	B/Fla.	12	Lab-Serv	Prot.	4	Yes
76	P	32	M	W	B/Fla.	9	Lab-Serv	Prot.	2	No
77	P	72	M	W	A/Fla.	2	Lab-Serv	Prot.	1	Yes
78	P	59	M	W	C/Fla.	9	Lab-Serv	Prot.	1	No
79	P	54	M	W	B/Fla.	19	Prof	Agnos.	0	Yes
80	P	52	M	W	C/Fla.	12	Cler-Sales	Prot.	4	Yes
81	P	54	M	W	C/Fla.	8	Lab-Serv	Prot.	1	No
82	P	46	M	B	D/Fla.	12	Cler-Sales	Prot.	3	Yes
83	P	49	M	W	B/Fla.	14	Lab-Serv	Cath.	3	Yes
84	P	70	M	W	C/Fla.	9	Cler-Sales	Cath.	4	No
85	P	45	M	W	B/Ga.	12	Lab-Serv	Prot.	3	No
86	P	56	M	W	C/Ga.	11	Lab-Serv	Prot.	1	No
87	P	56	M	W	D/Ga.	16	Cler-Sales	Prot.	4	Yes
88	P	58	F	W	C/Fla.	11	Cler-Sales	Prot.	3	Yes
89	P	27	M	W	B/Fla.	14	Lab-Serv	Prot.	1	Yes
90	P	64	M	W	B/Fla.	6	Lab-Serv	Prot.	4	No
91	P	44	M	W	A/Ga.	12	Prof	Mormon	4	Yes
92	P	28	M	B	B/Fla.	14	Prof	Prot.	2	No
93	P	60	M	W	B/Fla.	9	Lab-Serv	Prot.	4	No
94	P	23	M	W	C/Ga.	12	Lab-Serv	Prot.	2	Yes

95	P	60	M	W	B/Fla.	2	Lab-Serv	Prot.	3	Yes
96	P	55	M	W	D/Fla.	5	Lab-Serv	Agnos.	0	Yes
97	P	67	M	W	B/Fla.	19	Cler-Sales	Prot.	2	Yes
98	P	60	M	W	B/Fla.	8	Lab-Serv	Prot.	2	Yes
99	P	39	M	W	B/Ga.	14	Cler-Sales	Prot.	4	Yes
100	P	41	M	W	B/Ga..	12	Lab-Serv	Prot.	2	No
101	P	54	M	W	B/Fla.	12	Cler-Sales	Agnos.	0	No
102	P	17	F	W	B/Fla.	10	Lab-Serv	Prot.	2	No
103	P	76	F	W	B/Fla.	10	Lab-Serv	Prot.	4	No
104	P	17	F	B	A/Fla.	9	Lab-Serv	Prot.	3	Yes
105	P	61	M	W	B/Fla.	12	Cler-Sales	Prot.	2	No
106	P	37	M	W	B/Fla.	16	Prof	Prot.	1	Yes
107	P	75	F	W	D/Fla.	16	Cler-Sales	Prot.	4	No
108	P	73	F	B	B/Fla.	8	Lab-Serv	Prot.	4	Yes
109	P	59	M	W	B/Ga.	12	Lab-Serv	Prot.	4	Yes
110	P	68	F	W	B/Ga.	16	Cler-Sales	Prot.	3	Yes
111	P	53	M	W	B/Ga.	12	Lab-Serv	Prot.	2	Yes
112	P	63	M	W	D/Fla.	16	Cler-Sales	Prot.	3	No
113	P	52	M	W	B/Ga.	9	Cler-Sales	Prot.	1	Yes
114	P	62	M	W	A/Fla.	4	Lab-Serv	Prot.	4	Yes
115	P	57	M	W	B/Ga.	12	Lab-Serv	Prot.	4	Yes
116	P	51	M	W	B/Ga.	10	Lab-Serv	Prot.	1	No

**TABLE II: BACKGROUND CHARACTERISTICS OF PROSPECTIVELY INTERVIEWED
PATIENTS: COMPARISONS BETWEEN GROUPS WITH AND WITHOUT NDE**

	33 Patients with NDE	45 Patients without NDE
Mean Age (years)	49	53
Sex	26 Male (79%)	38 Male (84%)
	7 Female (21%)	7 Female (16%)
Race	33 White (100%)	41 White (91%)
		4 Black (9%)
Area of Residence (Southeastern U.S.)	32 (97%)	45 (100%)
Size of Community		
Rural	3 (9%)	4 (9%)
< 10,000	21 (64%)	27 (60%)
10,000 to 100,000	7 (21%)	9 (20%)
> 100,000	2 (6%)	5 (11%)
Mean Education (years)	12.3	11.5
Occupation		
Professional	5 (15%)	5 (11%)
Clerical-sales	10 (30%)	13 (29%)
Laborer-services	18 (55%)	27 (60%)
Religion		
Protestant	23 (70%)	38 (84%)
Catholic	4 (12%)	2 (5%)
Agnostic	5 (15%)	4 (9%)
Other	1 (3%)	1 (2%)
Frequency of Church Attendance[1]		
0	5 (15%)	4 (9%)
1-2	16 (49%)	18 (40%)
3-4	12 (36%)	23 (51%)
Previous Knowledge of NDE	4 (12%)	27 (60%) $p < .01$

[1] *Frequency of church attendance:* 0 = agnostic, 1 = none; 2 = less than monthly; 3 = 1 to 3
times per month; 4 = weekly.

TABLE III: BACKGROUND CHARACTERISTICS OF PATIENTS IN "THE GENERAL KNOWLEDGE" CONTROL STUDY

Interview Number	Age	Sex	Race	Residence[1]	Years of Education	Occupation[2]	Religion[3]	Frequency of Church Attendance[4]
1	55	M	B	C/Ga.	11	Lab-Serv	Prot.	4
2	57	M	W	B/Ga.	9	Lab-Serv	Prot.	2
3	57	M	W	D/Ga.	7	Lab-Serv	Prot.	4
4	71	M	W	B/Ga.	10	Cler-Sales	Prot.	3
5	50	M	W	D/Ga.	10	Cler-Sales	Prot.	4
6	57	M	W	C/Ga.	3	Lab-Serv	Prot.	3
7	55	M	B	C/Ga.	10	Lab-Serv	Prot.	4
8	76	M	B	D/Ga.	5	Lab-Serv	Prot.	4
9	57	M	W	D/Ga.	14	Prof	Prot.	0
10	56	M	W	D/Ga.	12	Cler-Sales	Agnos.	3
11	64	M	W	C/Ga.	8	Cler-Sales	Prot.	4
12	49	M	W	B/Ga.	8	Lab-Serv	Prot.	1
13	56	M	W	B/Ga.	10	Cler-Sales	Prot.	4
14	61	M	W	D/Ga.	11	Cler-Sales	Prot.	2
15	68	M	W	B/Ga.	15	Cler-Sales	Prot.	2
16	69	M	W	B/Ga.	9	Cler-Sales	Prot.	4
17	64	M	W	C/Ga.	12	Lab-Serv	Prot.	3
18	53	M	W	D/Ga.	9	Lab-Serv	Prot.	1
19	46	M	W	C/Ga.	15	Lab-Serv	Prot.	1
20	57	M	W	D/Ga.	9	Cler-Sales	Prot.	3
21	59	M	W	D/Ga.	19	Prof	Cath.	3
22	64	M	W	C/Ga.	12	Cler-Sales	Prot.	4
23	46	M	W	B/Ga.	7	Lab-Serv	Prot.	1
24	56	M	W	B/Ga.	11	Lab-Serv	Prot.	1
25	56	M	W	D/Ga.	16	Prof	Prot.	2

[1] Residence: Numerator—A = rural; B = township of < 10,000; C = city of 10,000 to 100,000; D = urban center of > 100,000.

[2] Occupation: Lab-Serv = laborer-services; Cler-Sales = clerical-sales; Prof = professional.

[3] Religion: Prot. = Protestant; Cath. = Catholic; Agnos. = agnostic.

[4] Frequency of Church Attendance: 0 = agnostic; 1 = none; 2 = less than monthly; 3 = 1 to 3 times per month; 4 = weekly

TABLE IV: CIRCUMSTANCES OF NEAR-DEATH CRISIS EVENTS

Interview Number[1]	Interval Between Crisis Event and Interview	Type of Crisis Event	Location of Crisis Event	Estimated Duration of Unconsciousness	Method of Resuscitation[2]
1	1 yr.	Arrest[3]	Hospital	1–30 min.	Meds
2	4 yr.	Arrest	Hospital	1–30 min.	Defib-Meds
3	4 yr.	Arrest	Hospital	1–30 min.	Defib-Meds
4	7 yr.	Arrest	Hospital	1–30 min.	Meds
5	4 yr.	Arrest	Hospital	1–30 min.	Meds
6	13 yr.	Accident	Auto	> 30 min.	Support
7	1 day	Arrest	Hospital	1–30 min.	Defib-Meds
8	7 yr.	Arrest	Hospital	> 30 min.	Defib-Meds
9	6 yr.	Arrest	Hospital	> 30 min.	Support
10	5 yr.	Arrest	Hospital	1–30 min.	Meds
11	1 yr.	Coma	Hospital	> 30 min.	Support
12	58 yr.	Coma	Hospital	> 30 min.	Support
13	1 day	Arrest	Hospital	> 30 min.	Defib-Meds
14	2 yr.	Arrest	Hospital	1–30 min.	Defib-Meds
15	1 yr.	Arrest	Hospital	> 30 min.	Defib-Meds
16	1 yr.	Arrest	Hospital	> 30 min.	Meds
17	1 yr.	Arrest	Hospital	1–30 min.	Meds
18	4 mo.	Coma	Hospital	> 30 min.	Support
19	4 yr.	Arrest	Hospital	1–30 min.	Defib-Meds

[1] *Interview Number:* "s" denotes surgical case.
[2] *Method of Resuscitation:* None = spontaneous recovery; Meds = medications; Defib-Meds = defibrillation plus medications; Support = chronic supportive care.
[3] *Arrest* = cardiac arrest.

20	1 mo.	Arrest	Parking Lot	1–30 min.	None
21	7 mo.	Arrest	Hospital	1–30 min.	Meds
22	1 mo.	Arrest	Hospital	1–30 min.	Defib-Meds
23	1 mo.	Coma	Hospital	> 30 min.	Support
24	1 mo.	Arrest	Hospital	1–30 min.	Defib-Meds
25	3 yr.	Arrest	Hospital	1–30 min.	Meds
26	4 yr.	Arrest	Hospital	1–30 min.	Meds
27	2 yr.	Arrest	Hospital	1–30 min.	Defib-Meds
28	2 yr.	Coma	Hospital	> 30 min.	Support
29	1 yr.	Arrest	Hospital	> 30 min.	Meds
30	12 hr.	Arrest	Hospital	< 1 min.	None
31	26 yr.	Accident	Hospital	> 30 min.	Support
32	5 yr.	Arrest	Hospital	1–30 min.	Defib-Meds
33	1 yr.	Arrest	Hospital	1–30 min.	Defib-Meds
34	2 wk.	Arrest	Hospital	1–30 min.	Defib-Meds
35	45 yr.	Coma	Hospital	> 30 min.	Support
36	40 yr.	Coma	Hospital	> 30 min.	Support
37	17 yr.	Coma	Hospital	> 30 min.	Support
38	23 yr.	Coma	Hospital	1–30 min.	Support
39s	1 yr.	Surgery	Hospital	1–30 min.	Support
40s	1 yr.	Surgery	Hospital	> 30 min.	Support
41	19 yr.	Coma	Hospital	1–30 min.	Support
42	2 yr.	Arrest	Hospital	1–30 min.	Meds
43	1 yr.	Arrest	Hospital	> 30 min.	Defib-Meds
44	1 yr.	Coma	Hospital	> 30 min.	Support
45	15 yr.	Coma	Hospital	1–30 min.	Support
46	48 yr.	Coma	Hospital	> 30 min.	Support
47	8 yr.	Arrest	Hospital	1–30 min.	Defib-Meds
48s	22 yr.	Surgery	Hospital	> 30 min.	Support
49	1 yr.	Coma	Hospital	1–30 min.	Support

TABLE IV: (cont'd)

Interview Number	Interval Between Crisis Event and Interview	Type of Crisis Event	Location of Crisis Event	Estimated Duration of Unconsciousness	Method of Resuscitation
50s	25 yr.	Surgery	Hospital	> 30 min.	Support
51s	4 yr.	Surgery	Hospital	> 30 min.	Support
52	2 yr.	Accident	Auto	> 30 min.	Support
53	1 yr.	Coma	Ambulance	> 30 min.	Support
54	11 yr.	Coma	Hospital	> 30 min.	Support
55s	1 yr.	Surgery	Hospital	> 30 min.	Support
56	2 mo.	Arrest	Hospital	1–30 min.	Defib-Meds
57	1 yr.	Arrest	Hospital	1–30 min.	Defib-Meds
58s	2 yr.	Surgery	Hospital	> 30 min.	Support
59s	37 yr.	Surgery	Hospital	> 30 min.	Support
60	10 yr.	Arrest	Hospital	1–30 min.	Defib-Meds
61	8 yr.	Arrest	Hospital	1–30 min.	Defib-Meds
62	7 yr.	Arrest	Auto	1–30 min.	Meds
63	1 yr.	Arrest	Hospital	1–30 min.	Defib-Meds
64	3 yr.	Suicide	Hospital	> 30 min.	Support
65	8 yr.	Coma	Hospital	1–30 min.	Meds
66	1 yr.	Arrest	Hospital	1–30 min.	Defib-Meds
67	1 yr.	Arrest	Hospital	> 30 min.	Defib-Meds
68	10 yr.	Accident	Vietnam	> 30 min.	Support
69	14 yr.	Accident	Vietnam	> 30 min.	Support
70s	7 yr.	Surgery	Hospital	> 30 min.	Support
71s	4½ yr.	Surgery	Hospital	> 30 min.	Defib-Meds
72	4 mo.	Arrest	Home	1–30 min.	None
73	1 mo.	Arrest	Home	1–30 min.	None

74	1 day	Arrest	Hospital	1–30 min.	Defib-Meds
75	1 day	Arrest	Hospital	< 1 min.	Meds
76	2 wk.	Arrest	Hospital	< 1 min.	Defib-Meds
77	1 mo.	Arrest	Home	< 1 min.	None
78	2 yr.	Arrest	Hospital	1–30 min.	Defib-Meds
79	5 yr.	Arrest	Home	1–30 min.	Meds
80	1 yr.	Arrest	Hospital	1–30 min.	Defib-Meds
81	4 mo.	Arrest	Home	1–30 min.	Defib-Meds
82	3 yr.	Arrest	Auto	< 1 min.	None
83	3 yr.	Arrest	Hospital	< 1 min.	Meds
84	2 wk.	Arrest	Hospital	< 1 min.	None
85	1 day	Arrest	Hospital	< 1 min.	Meds
86	1 mo.	Arrest	Hospital	> 30 min.	Defib-Meds
87	1 mo.	Arrest	Hospital	1–30 min.	Defib-Meds
88	2 wk.	Arrest	Hospital	< 1 min.	Meds
89	1 yr.	Coma	Hospital	> 30 min.	Support
90	2 wk.	Arrest	Hospital	1–30 min.	Meds
91	2 mo.	Arrest	Hospital	< 1 min.	None
92	9 yr.	Accident	Vietnam	1–30 min.	None
93	1 mo.	Arrest	Boat	< 1 min.	None
94	1 yr.	Arrest	Hospital	1–30 min.	Defib-Meds
95	1 mo.	Arrest	Home	1–30 min.	Meds
96	1 mo.	Arrest	Hospital	1–30 min.	Defib-Meds
97	1 yr.	Arrest	Home	< 1 min.	None
98	4 day	Arrest	Hospital	> 30 min.	Defib-Meds
99	5 mo.	Arrest	Hospital	1–30 min.	Meds
100	1 yr.	Coma	Hospital	> 30 min.	Meds
101	15 yr.	Arrest	Hospital	1–30 min.	Meds
102	1 mo.	Arrest	Hospital	> 30 min.	Defib-Meds
103	11 day	Arrest	Hospital	1–30 min.	Defib-Meds

TABLE IV: (cont'd)

Interview Number	Interval Between Crisis Event and Interview	Type of Crisis Event	Location of Crisis Event	Estimated Duration of Unconsciousness	Method of Resuscitation
104	16 day	Coma	Hospital	1–30 min.	Support
105	1 mo.	Arrest	Hospital	> 30 min.	Defib-Meds
106	3 mo.	Arrest	Hospital	1–30 min.	Defib-Meds
107	2 wk.	Arrest	Hospital	1–30 min.	Defib-Meds
108	5 wk.	Arrest	Home	< 1 min.	None
109	6 yr.	Arrest	Home	1–30 min.	Meds
110	2 wk.	Arrest	Hospital	< 1 min.	None
111	2 yr.	Arrest	Hospital	1–30 min.	Meds
112	4 mo.	Arrest	Hospital	1–30 min.	Meds
113	1 mo.	Arrest	Hospital	1–30 min.	Defib-Meds
114	2 yr.	Accident	Auto	> 30 min.	Support
115	1 yr.	Arrest	Hospital	1–30 min.	Defib-Meds
116	3 mo.	Arrest	Hospital	1–30 min.	Defib-Meds

TABLE V: CIRCUMSTANCES OF THE SURGICAL CRISIS EVENTS

Interview Number	Type of Experience	Surgical Circumstances
19s*	Autoscopy	Open-heart surgery in 1978 without known complication
28s*	Autoscopy	Gall bladder surgery in 1968 without known complication
39s	Transcendence	Oral surgery in 1976 with severe allergic reaction to anesthetic
40s	Transcendence	Hysterectomy in 1977; possible cardiac difficulties (records not available)
48s	Transcendence	Complications at childbirth in 1955
50s	Transcendence	Complications at childbirth (breech delivery) in 1952, associated with severe toxemia of pregnancy
51s	Transcendence	Kidney surgery (nephrectomy) in 1973, with laceration of spleen and emergency splenectomy
55s	Transcendence	Surgical repair of a ruptured abdominal aortic aneurysm in 1976, associated with hemorrhagic shock (blood pressure 40/0)
58s	Transcendence	Surgical removal of ovarian cyst in 1976 without known complication
59s	Transcendence	Caesarean section in 1940, associated with prolonged labor and shock
68s*	Autoscopy	Emergency amputation of leg in Vietnam in 1969, associated with severe hemorrhagic shock
70s	Autoscopy	Lumbar disk surgery in 1972, associated with cardiac irregularity
71s	Transcendence	Open-heart surgery in 1975, associated with cardiac arrest

*NDEs occurring during *non*surgical crisis events were also reported by these persons and are discussed elsewhere.

**TABLE VI: CIRCUMSTANCES OF THE NEAR-DEATH CRISIS EVENT IN
PROSPECTIVELY INTERVIEWED, NONSURGICAL PATIENTS: COMPARISONS
BETWEEN GROUPS WITH AND WITHOUT NDE**

	33 Patients with NDE	45 Patients without NDE	
Type			
Cardiac Arrest	26 (79%)	40 (89%)	
Coma	5 (15%)	3 (7%)	
Accident	2 (6%)	2 (4%)	
Location			
Hospital	31 (94%)	32 (71%)	$p < .02$
Estimated Duration of Unconsciousness			
Less than 1 minute	1 (3%)	13 (29%)	$p < .01$
1 to 30 minutes	19 (58%)	25 (56%)	
Greater than 30 minutes	13 (39%)	7 (15%)	$p < .02$
Method of Resuscitation			
None	2 (6%)	11 (24%)	$p < .05$
Medications	10 (30%)	13 (29%)	
Defibrillation-Medications	13 (39%)	18 (40%)	
Supportive	8 (25%)	3 (7%)	$p < .05$

TABLE VII: CIRCUMSTANCES OF ADDITIONAL NEAR-DEATH CRISIS EVENTS

Interview Number	Additional Near-Death Crisis Events	Associated Near-Death Experiences
2	8–10 cardiac arrests	None
4	1 cardiac arrest	None
5	1 coma	Same type of NDE (see Table VIII)
11	1 cardiac arrest	None
12	1 cardiac arrest	None
14	1 cardiac arrest	None
16	1 coma	Same type of NDE (see Table VIII)
18	3–5 comas	Same type of NDE each time (see Table VIII)
19	1 cardiac arrest	None
20	5–10 cardiac arrests	None
28	1 coma	Same type of NDE (see Table VIII)
45	1 cardiac arrest	Same type of NDE (see Table VIII)
54	3 comas	NDEs during 2 comas: 1. Contained elements 1, 2, 3, 4, 10 (see Table IX) 2. Contained elements 1, 2, 3, 4, 10 (see Table IX)
60	1 cardiac arrest	None
62	8–10 assorted: accidents, cardiac arrests, comas	Same NDE each time (see Table VIII)
63	1 cardiac arrest	NDE containing elements 1, 2, 3, 5, 7, 8, 9, 10 (see Table IX)
66	1 cardiac arrest	None
73	5–10 cardiac arrests	None
77	1 cardiac arrest	None
82	1 cardiac arrest	None
84	1 cardiac arrest	None
88	1 cardiac arrest	None
89	1 cardiac arrest	None
91	5–10 cardiac arrests	None
93	1 cardiac arrest	None
96	1 cardiac arrest	None
97	1 cardiac arrest	None
101	1 cardiac arrest	None
105	1 cardiac arrest	None
106	1 cardiac arrest	None
108	5–10 cardiac arrests	None
110	2 cardiac arrests	None
113	1 cardiac arrest	None

TABLE VIII: TYPE AND ELEMENTS OF THE NEAR-DEATH EXPERIENCE

Interview Number[1]	Type of NDE[2]	1	2	3	4	5	6	7	8	9	10
1	Auto.	X	X	X	X						X
2	Trans.	X	X	X					X		X
3	Comb.	X	X	X	X	X		X		X	X
4	Trans.	X	X	X					X		X
5	Auto.	X	X	X	X						X
6	Auto.	X	X	X	X						X
7	Trans.	X	X	X						X	X
8	Comb.	X	X	X	X	X		X	X	X	X
9	Trans.		X	X					X	X	X
10	Trans.	X	X	X							X
11	Auto.	X	X	X	X						X
12	Auto.	X	X	X	X						X
13	Auto.		X	X	X						X
14	Auto.	X	X	X	X						X
15	Trans.	X	X	X		X	X	X	X	X	X
16	Comb.	X	X	X	X				X	X	X
17	Comb.	X	X	X	X			X	X	X	X
18	Trans.	X	X	X					X	X	X
19	Auto.	X	X	X	X					X	X
20	Auto.	X	X	X	X						X
21	Trans.	X	X	X		X		X		X	X
22	Trans.	X	X	X		X		X			X
23	Auto.	X	X	X	X						X
24	Trans.	X	X	X					X	X	X
25	Trans.	X	X	X					X	X	X
26	Trans.	X	X	X		X					X
27	Comb.	X	X	X	X	X			X		X
28	Auto.	X	X	X	X						X
29	Trans.	X	X	X		X				X	X
30	Auto.	X	X	X	X						X
31	Auto.	X	X	X	X						X
32	Auto.		X	X	X						X
33	Trans.	X	X	X		X		X			X
34	Trans.	X	X	X					X	X	X
35	Comb.	X	X	X	X				X	X	X
36	Trans.		X	X				X	X		X
37	Trans.	X	X	X					X	X	X

[1] *Interview Number:* "s" denotes surgical case.

[2] Auto. = autoscopic; Trans. = transcendental; Comb. = combined.

TABLE VIII: (cont'd)

Interview Number	Type of NDE	Elements of NDE (see Table IX)									
		1	2	3	4	5	6	7	8	9	10
38	Trans.	X	X	X		X		X			X
39s	Trans.	X	X	X					X	X	X
40s	Trans.	X	X	X			X	X	X	X	X
41	Comb.	X	X	X	X	X			X	X	X
42	Auto.	X	X	X	X						X
43	Trans.	X	X	X		X		X	X	X	X
44	Trans.	X	X	X					X	X	X
45	Comb.	X	X	X	X	X					X
46	Auto.	X	X	X	X						X
47	Trans.	X	X	X					X		X
48s	Trans.	X	X	X			X	X		X	X
49	Trans.	X	X	X		X		X			X
50s	Trans.	X	X	X		X			X	X	X
51s	Trans.	X	X	X		X					X
52	Trans.	X	X	X					X	X	X
53	Comb.	X	X	X	X				X		X
54	Trans.	X	X	X					X	X	X
55s	Trans.	X	X					X	X		X
56	Trans.	X	X	X		X		X		X	X
57	Comb.	X	X	X	X			X	X	X	X
58s	Trans.		X	X						X	X
59s	Trans.	X	X	X					X	X	X
60	Comb.	X	X	X	X			X	X		X
61	Trans.	X	X	X					X	X	X
62	Trans.	X	X	X					X	X	X
63	Auto.	X	X	X	X						X
64	Auto.	X	X	X	X						X
65	Trans.	X	X	X				X	X	X	X
66	Trans.	X	X	X					X	X	X
67	Auto.	X	X	X	X						X
68	Comb.	X	X	X	X		X	X		X	X
69	Auto.		X	X	X						X
70s	Auto.	X	X	X	X						X
71s	Trans.	X	X	X					X	X	X

**TABLE IX: ELEMENTS OF THE NDE AND THEIR FREQUENCY
OF OCCURRENCE IN 61 NONSURGICAL CASES**

Element	Frequency
1. Subjective sense of being dead	92%
2. Predominant emotional content of calm and peace	100%
3. Sense of bodily separation	100%
4. Observation of physical objects and events (autoscopy)	53%
5. Dark region or void	23%
6. Life review	3%
7. The light	28%
8. Entering a transcendental environment	54%
9. Encountering others	48%
10. Return	100%

TABLE X: BACKGROUND CHARACTERISTICS OF THE 61 NONSURGICAL CASES REPORTING ON NDE: COMPARISONS BETWEEN GROUPS AS TO ELEMENTS (1–10) FOUND IN NDEs

Background Characteristics	Groupings	Summary of Comparisons
Age	3 groups: 20–40; 41–60; 61–80 years	No significant differences in NDE elements between groups
Sex	2 groups: male; female	Females > Males, element 9 ($p < .02$); otherwise, no significant differences between groups
Race	2 groups: white; black	Too few blacks for comparison
Area of Residence	2 groups: Southeastern U.S.; other U.S.	No significant differences in NDE elements between groups
Size of Home Community	4 groups: rural; < 10,000; 10,000–100,000; > 100,000	No significant differences in NDE elements between groups
Education (Years)	3 groups: < 10; 10–12; > 12	No significant differences in NDE elements between highest (> 12) and lowest (< 10) education groups
Occupation	3 groups: laborer-services; clerical-sales; professional	Laborer-services > professional, element 9 ($p < .05$); otherwise, no significant differences in NDE elements between groups
Religion	3 groups: Protestant; Catholic; agnostic	No significant differences in NDE elements between groups
Frequency of Church Attendance	3 groups: agnostic; none to < monthly; 1–4 times per month	No significant differences in NDE elements between groups
Previous Knowledge of NDE	2 groups: yes; no	Too few "yes" responses for comparison

**TABLE XI: CIRCUMSTANCES OF NEAR-DEATH CRISIS EVENT IN THE
61 NONSURGICAL CASES REPORTING ON NDE: COMPARISONS BETWEEN
GROUPS AS TO ELEMENTS (1–10) FOUND IN NDEs**

Near-Death Crisis Event	Groupings	Summary of Comparisons
Type	3 groups: cardiac arrest; coma; accident	No significant differences in NDE elements between groups
Location	2 groups: in-hospital; out-of-hospital	Too few out-of-hospital cases for comparison
Estimated Length of Unconsciousness	3 groups: < 1 minute; 1–30 minutes; > 30 minutes	No significant differences in NDE elements between groups
Method of Resuscitation	4 groups: none; medications; defibrillation-medications; support	No significant differences in NDE elements between groups
Interval Between Crisis Event and Interview	4 groups: 1 month or less; 1 month to 1 year; 1 to 5 years; > 5 years	No significant differences between 1 month or less group and > 5 years group

TABLE XII: DESCRIPTIONS OF THE TRANSCENDENTAL ENVIRONMENT

Interview	Description
2	A "road" which ended at an "old farm gate"
4	"Clouds . . . gray-white clouds"
8	"Deep blue" sky with an occasional "cloud"
9	"Beautiful flowers" in a flowerbed
15	"Steps" leading to the "Golden Gates of Heaven"
16	Beautiful "park" with "hill, trees and flowers"
17	"Just another world . . . bright sunny world . . . real beautiful"
18	"Still stream of water" with "rainbow colors in background"
24	"Beautiful blue sky . . . field of flowers of different colors"
25	"The world split"—everything was "silver . . . like diamonds and stars"
27	"Walking on clouds . . . [during] a clear, beautiful summer day with clear sky"
34	"Water" with a "beautiful sunglow . . . trees . . . shadows of gold"
35	"A place of beautiful light that pulsated with exquisite music"
36	"Clouds"
37	"Mist" with gentle wind blowing
41	"Long corridor which became all light"
43	"Gates of heaven" with "people on other side of gate"
44	"Clouds . . . dark and bright clouds"
47	A "fence" dividing "extremely scraggly territory" from "the most beautiful pasture scene"
52	Landscape full of people "of all different nationalities . . . all working on their arts and crafts"
53	"Golden gates" which were closed at the time
54	"Top of a mountain . . . just beautiful up there . . . ethereal beauty"
57	"Flowers, trees of all kinds, beautiful flower gardens, the sun was beautiful . . . a tremendous happiness thing"
60	"Clouds . . . with a bright light"
61	"Billowy cloud, cottony cloud . . . gold, ornamental gate, wrought-iron . . . with a highly polished gold color"
62	Aside the "Sea of Galilee" under a "beautiful tree"
65	Beautiful "panorama . . . just beyond words"
66	"Beautiful green pasture . . . cattle grazing . . . bright sunshiny day"

TABLE XIII: THE SPIRIT OR PRESENCE ENCOUNTERED IN THE
TRANSCENDENTAL NEAR-DEATH EXPERIENCE

Interview	Identity of Spirit or Presence	Summary of Communication
3	Presence of God	Asked God for more time with children in "clear loud voice"
8	Spirits of living children	None
	Presence of God	God said in "loud, thundering" voice . . . "Go back," work not done yet
9	Spirit of unknown priest	Verbal conversation with priest about living or dying
15	Presence of Jesus	"Words were spoken to me" but content cannot be recalled
16	Spirit of deceased father	"Urged" by father's nonverbal gestures to "come on"
17	Spirits of Lord and deceased relatives and friends	All spirits, with "their hands up, waving," said, "Go back . . . Your children and a lot of people are going to need you"
18	Spirits of deceased relatives	Spirits "push me back" and "tell me it's not time yet"
19	Presence of deceased older brother	Brother presented a choice of either "staying" or "returning to body"
21	Presence of four unknown nurses	Verbal interrogation by nurses about possible "subversive activities"
24	Spirit of living granddaughter	None
25	Spirits of deceased mother and Christ	Spirits beckoned with their hands and said, "Come on home, come on home"
29	Spirit of deceased father	Father said, "Go back and stay with your sister. Everything is going to work out"
34	Spirits of deceased relatives	Greeted by deceased husband with "outstretched arms"—no conversation
35	Presence of God	"I told God in my prayers I wanted to go but was needed here"
37	Spirit of deceased father	Father said, "Go back to your mother for a while"
38	Presence of "many personalities"	None
41	Spirit of the Lord	Asked Lord, "Please don't take me now. Let me stay and raise my kids"
43	Spirits of Jesus and unknown people	Jesus said, "You have one little black spot you have to clean up and then I will come get you. Go back."

TABLE XIII: (cont'd)

Interview	Identity of Spirit or Presence	Summary of Communication
44	Spirits of deceased relatives	"It seems like they were greeting me . . . their arms out for me to come to them." Grandmother said, "We'll see you later but not this time"
52	Spirits of two unknown men	Spirits said, "We're here to show you the way . . . If you do not wish to go, we've got to get on. We'll be back for you"
54	Unknown presence	"Voice" said, "You can't go yet. You have unfinished business"
56	Spirits of two unknown men	None
57	Spirits of deceased relatives	None
61	Spirit of unknown "Roman" man	None
62	Spirit of God	God said, "It's all right, dear, you'll make it. I'm not ready for you yet"
65	Presence of "angel"	"Total communication without saying anything"
66	Spirit of "shepherd"	None
68	Presence of deceased war comrades	All expressed (without words) "no sympathy, no sorrow . . . didn't want to go back . . . happy"

**TABLE XIV: EFFECT OF NEAR-DEATH CRISIS
EVENT[1] ON FEAR OF DEATH AND BELIEF IN
AFTERLIFE**

Fear of Death	With NDE (61 Subjects)	Without NDE (45 Subjects)	
Increased	0	5	
No Change	11	39	$p < .001$
Decreased	50	1	$p < .001$

Belief in Afterlife	With NDE (61 Subjects)	Without NDE (45 Subjects)	
Increased	47	0	
No Change	14	45	$p < .001$
Decreased	0	0	$p < .001$

[1] Surgical cases not included.

**TABLE XV: FOLLOW-UP STUDY ON EFFECT OF NEAR-DEATH CRISIS
EVENT ON FEAR OF DEATH IN 44 SUBJECTS[1]**

	With NDE (26 Subjects)	Without NDE (18 Subjects)	
Score on Templer Death Anxiety Scale[2]	3.62	6.39	p < .001
Score on Dickstein Death Concern Scale[3]	58.1	68.6	p < .005

STANDARD RATINGS:

Death Anxiety	Low	"Normal"	High
Templer Scale	—	6.77	11.62
Dickstein Scale	58.8	74.3	88.8

[1] Forty-four subjects from the NDE study who returned the scales. The groups with (26 subjects) and without (18 subjects) an NDE were comparable in age, sex, race, area of residence, years of education, occupation, religion, and frequency of church attendance.

[2] D. I. Templer, "The Construction and Validation of a Death Anxiety Scale," *J Gen Psychol* 82: 165, 1970.

[3] L. S. Dickstein, "Death Concern: Measurement and Correlates," *Psychol Rep* 30: 563, 1972.

References

Epigraph: L. Thomas, "Facts of Life," *New Engl J Med* 1977. Reprinted by permission.

Preface

1. G. E. Burch, et al., "What Death Is Like," *Am Heart J* 76:438, 1968. Reprinted by permission.

Chapter 1: Beginnings

1. R. A. Moody, Jr., *Life After Life* (Covington, Ga.: Mockingbird Books, 1975).
2. J. G. Robson, "Measurement of Depth of Anaesthesia," *Br J Anaesth* 41: 785, 1969.
3. R. S. Blacher, "On Awakening Paralyzed During Surgery—A Syndrome of Traumatic Neurosis," *JAMA* 234: 67, 1975.
4. M. S. Gaevskaya, *Biochemistry of the Brain During the Process of Dying and Resuscitation* (New York: Consultants Bureau, 1964).
5. D. I. Templer, "The Construction and Validation of a Death Anxiety Scale," *J Gen Psychol* 82: 165, 1970.
6. L. S. Dickstein, "Death Concern: Measurement and Correlates," *Psychol Rep* 30: 563, 1972.

Chapter 6: Surgical Experiences

1. Blacher, loc. cit.
2. I. Silbergleit, "On Awakening Paralyzed During Surgery" (letter), *JAMA* 235: 1209, 1976.
3. H. D. Messer, ibid., 1210.
4. D. B. Cheek, "What Does the Surgically Anesthetized Patient Hear?" *Rocky Mountain Med J* 57: 49, 1960.

Chapter 9: Implications of the Near-Death Experience

1. H. E. Stephenson, Jr., *Cardiac Arrest and Resuscitation,* 4th ed. (St. Louis: C. V. Mosby Co., 1974, p. 733. Quote from R. L. MacMillan and K. W. Brown, "Cardiac Arrest Remembered," *Can Med Assoc J* 104: 889, 1971.
2. A. D. Weisman and T. P. Hackett, "Predilection to Death," *Psychosomatic Med* 23: 247, 1961. Copyright 1961 by The American Psychosomatic Society, Inc. Reprinted by permission of the publisher.
3. H. Feifel, S. Hanson, R. Jones and L. Edwards, in *Proceedings 75th Annual Conv APA,* 1967, p. 201.
4. J. Gosselin, E. Perez and A. Gagnon, in *Psychiatr J Univ Ottawa* 2: 120, 1977.
5. C. A. Garfield, "Elements of Psychosocial Oncology: Doctor-Patient Relationships in Terminal Illness," in *Psychosocial Care of the Dying Patient* (New York: McGraw-Hill, 1978), p. 103.
6. A. S. Relman, "Laetrilomania—Again," *New Engl J Med* 298: 215, 1978. Reprinted by permission.
7. J. L. Verrilli, "Laetrile" (letter), *New Engl J Med* 298: 854, 1978. Reprinted by permission.
8. J. G. Scott, ibid. Reprinted by permission.
9. Gosselin, Perez and Gagnon, loc. cit.
10. E. Kübler-Ross, *On Death and Dying* (New York: Macmillan, 1969).
11. V. H. Hine, "Altered States of Consciousness: A Form of Death Education," *Death Education* 1: 377–396, Washington, D.C.: © Hemisphere Publishing Corp., 1978. Reprinted by permission of the publisher.
12. A. N. Exton-Smith and M. D. Cautab, "Terminal Illness in the Aged," *The Lancet* 2: 305, 1961. Reprinted by permission.
13. J. H. Phillips, Panel presentations in *Caring for the Dying Patient and His Family* (New York: Health Sciences Publishing Corporation, 1973), p. 45.
14. Weisman and Hackett, op. cit., p. 232.
15. L. Thomas, "A Meliorist View of Disease and Dying," *J Med Philos* 1: 212, 1976.
16. W. B. Cannon, *Am Anthropologist* 44: 72, 1942.

17. C. Richter, in *The Meaning of Death,* ed. Herman Feifel (New York: McGraw-Hill, 1959).

Chapter 10: Explanation

1. R. Kastenbaum, "Temptations from the Everafter," *Human Behavior,* September 1977, p. 28. Reprinted by permission.
2. R. S. Blacher, "To Sleep, Perchance to Dream . . ." *JAMA* 242: 2291, 1979. Copyright 1979, American Medical Association. Reprinted by permission.
3. M. B. Sabom, "Near-Death Experiences" (letter), *JAMA* 244: 29, 1980. Copyright 1980, American Medical Association. Reprinted by permission.
4. Kastenbaum, op. cit., p. 30. Reprinted by permission.
5. B. M. Dlin, A. Stern and S. J. Poliakoff, "Survivors of Cardiac Arrest: The First Few Days," *Psychosomatics* 15: 61, 1974.
6. S. Freud, "Thoughts for the Times on War and Death," in *Collected Papers,* vol. 4 (New York: Basic Books, 1959).
7. R. Noyes, Jr., and R. Kletti, "Depersonalization in the Face of Life-Threatening Danger: An Interpretation," *Omega, Journal of Death and Dying* 7: 103, 1976. Reprinted by permission.
8. R. Noyes, Jr., "Depersonalization in the Face of Life-Threatening Danger: A Description," *Psychiatry* 39: 19, 1976. Reprinted by permission.
9. R. Noyes, Jr., "The Experience of Dying," *Psychiatry* 35: 181, 1972.
10. R. S. Blacher, loc. cit. Reprinted by permission.
11. R. Noyes, Jr., and D. J. Slymen, "The Subjective Response to Life-Threatening Danger," *Omega, Journal of Death and Dying* 9: 4, 1979. Reprinted by permission.
12. R. Noyes, Jr., "Near Death Experiences: Their Interpretation and Significance," in *Between Life and Death,* ed. R. Kastenbaum (New York: Springer, 1978).
13. A. Lukianowicz, "Autoscopic Phenomena," *Arch Neurol Psychiatry* 80: 199, 1958. Copyright 1958, American Medical Association. Reprinted by permission.
14. Ibid., p. 200. Reprinted by permission.
15. Ibid., p. 202. Reprinted by permission.
16. Personal communication.
17. S. Freud, *The Interpretation of Dreams* (New York: Avon Books, 1965), p. 576.
18. N. Schnaper, "Comments Germane to the Paper Entitled 'The Reality of Death Experiences' by Ernst Rodin," *J Nerv Ment Dis* 168: 269, 1980. © 1980 The Williams & Wilkins Co., Baltimore, Md. Reprinted by permission.

19. Personal communication.
20. Personal communication.
21. L. Thomas, "A Meliorist View of Disease and Dying," *J Med Philos* 1: 212, 1976.
22. T. Oyama, T. Ji and R. Yamaya, "Profound Analgesic Effects of B-Endorphin in Man," *The Lancet* 8160: 122–4, 1980.
23. Ibid., p. 123.
24. Personal communication.
25. L. Roberts, "Activation and Interference of Cortical Functions," in *Electrical Stimulation of the Brain*, ed. D. E. Sheer (Austin: University of Texas Press, 1961), p. 547.
26. W. Penfield, "The Role of the Temporal Cortex in Certain Psychical Phenomena," *J Ment Sci* 101: 451, 1955.
27. Schnaper, loc. cit. Reprinted by permission.
28. A. M. Ludwig, "Altered States of Consciousness," *Arch Gen Psychiat* 15: 225, 1966. Copyright 1966, American Medical Association. Reprinted by permission.
29. Y. Henderson and H. W. Haggard, *Noxious Gases and the Principles of Respiration Influencing Their Action* (New York: American Chemical Society, 1927).
30. R. A. McFarland, "The Psychological Effects of Oxygen Deprivation (Anoxaemia) on Human Behavior, "*Arch Psychol* (Columbia University) 145, 1932.
31. L. J. Meduna, "The Effect of Carbon Dioxide upon the Functions of the Brain," in *Carbon Dioxide Therapy* (Springfield, Ill.: Charles C. Thomas, 1950), pp. 23, 24, 28.
32. Ibid., p. 19.
33. Ibid., p. 35.

Chapter 11: Thoughts on the Meaning of the Near-Death Experience

1. R. S. Blacher, "Near-Death Experiences" (letter), *JAMA* 244: 30, 1980. Copyright 1980, American Medical Association. Reprinted by permission.
2. W. B. Weimer, "Manifestations of Mind," in *Consciousness and the Brain*, G. G. Globus, G. Maxwell and I. Savodnik, eds. (New York: Plenum Press, 1976), p. 18.
3. W. Penfield, *The Mystery of the Mind* (Princeton N.J., Princeton University Press, 1975), p. 73.
4. Ibid., pp. 39, 47.
5. Ibid., pp. 85, 48.
6. Gaevskaya, op. cit.
7. A. Einstein, *The Human Side*, Helen Dukas and Banesh Hoffmann, eds. (Princeton, N.J.: Princeton University Press, 1979), p. 33.

Index

Academy of Medical Sciences, U.S.S.R.,
    Laboratory of Experimental Physiol-
    ogy of Resuscitation, 8
accident, as research category, 56, 58
"afterexperiences" (recurrent autoscopic en-
    counters), 116–123
afterlife beliefs, NDEs and, 60–61, 185,
    212
"afterworld," perceptions of, 6, 11, 19, 27,
    38, 44–46, 51, 54
age changes:
    of separated self, 22
    of spirits of deceased, 48–49
altered states of consciousness, NDEs and,
    144, 174–178
    causes of, 175
    epileptogenic discharges and, 173–174,
    182
    Ludwig's definition of, 175
    medications and, 168–171
"Altered States of Consciousness" (Lud-
    wig), 174–175
"Altered States of Consciousness: A Form
    of Death Education" (Hine), 144
A.M.A. Archives of Neurology and Psychia-
    try, 164
American Anthropologist, 147

American Cancer Society, CITE in, 141
anesthesia:
    "crisis event," experienced under, 56
    pain sensations and, 31
    unconscious and, 63
animal experiments, in psychology of death,
    148
anthropology, psychic death studied in,
    147–148
Archives of General Psychiatry, 175
Ascension to the Empyrean (Bosch), 38
Atlanta Veterans Administration Center, 13
"Attitude of Psychiatrists Toward Termi-
    nally Ill Patients," (Gosselin, Perez,
    and Gagnon), 140, 142
Audette, John, 184n
auditory perceptions in NDEs, 17, 18, 20,
    26, 31–32, 40, 53
    semiconscious state and, 153–156
    in surgical procedures, 65–66, 70, 73,
    74–75, 80
Australian aborigines, psychic death among,
    147
autoscopic NDEs, 24–37, 56
    attempted communication with others in,
    32–33
    author's hypothesis about, 184–185

autoscopic NDEs *(cont.)*
    critical evaluation of, 81–115, 154–178
    hearing in, *see* auditory perceptions in
        NDEs
    out-of-body experience vs., 27
    recurrent, 116–123
    "return" to physical body and, 34–36
    semiconscious perceptions and, 115, 154–
        156
    "thought travel" in, 33–34
    transcendental elements combined with,
        52–54, 185
    visual details noted in, *see* visual percep-
        tions in NDEs
    voluntary movement in, 33
    witnesses' verification of, 36–37, 68–69,
        71, 72, 75, 99, 112–113, 159, 184
"Autoscopic Phenomena" (Lukianowicz),
    164
autoscopic surgical experiences, 64–75
    medical account of procedure and, 67–68,
        71, 73–74
    observation of physical objects and events
        in, 64–67, 69–70, 72–73, 74–75, 80
    out-of-body perceptions in, 64–67, 69–70,
        72–73, 74–75
    in patient's comparison with NDE, 67,
        74
    pleasant responses in, 69, 74
    subjective sense of being dead in, 73
    surgeon's-patient's comparison of, 68–69,
        71
    unpleasant responses in, 65, 66
B-endorphin, 171–173
biofeedback, 183
biological death, 8
Blacher, Richard S., 79–80, 152, 162, 179–
    180
Blake, William, 25
"blacking out," 7
Bosch, Hieronymus, 38
brain:
    chemistry and functioning of, 171–178
    computer mechanism in, 182, 183, 184
    medications affecting, 168–171
    mind mechanism in, 181–184
"brain death," 8

cancer treatment, doctor-patient relationship
    in, 141–142
Cannon, Walter B., 147
cardiac arrest:
    hypercarbia in, 176–178
    hypoxia in, 175–176
    patient's knowledge of resuscitation meth-
        ods in, 83–114, 195
    as research category, 56, 58, 59
    Stokes-Adams syndrome in, 162

cardiology, technological basis of, 2
cardioversion, in semiconscious state vs.
    post-NDE condition, 154–155
Cheek, David, 80
"clinical death," defining of, 8–9
cognitive processes, *see* thinking, clarity of
coma, as research category, 56, 58
combined NDEs, 52–54, 185
Connecticut, University of, 184*n*
consciousness, mind-brain dualism and,
    181–184, 185
content of NDEs, 6, 206
    dark region or void as perception in, 10,
        20, 40, 41–43, 53
    encounters with "spiritual beings" in, 11,
        22, 23, 44, 46–50, 210–211
    life review in, 10, 40, 50
    light as perception in, 10–11, 40, 42, 43–
        44, 53–54
    observation of physical objects and events
        in, 10, 15, 17, 18, 19, 20, 21–22, 25–
        34, 36–37, 53
    predominant emotions in, 10, 18–20, 21,
        23, 29, 40, 41, 76, 78, 145, 148–150,
        174
    research analyses of, 59–60, 83–115,
        153–178, 206, 209–211
    "return" as perception in, 11, 17–18, 34–
        36, 50–52, 54
    sense of bodily separation in, 10, 16, 17,
        19, 20–22, 23, 25–27, 45, 47, 50, 53;
        see also autoscopic NDEs
    subjective sense of being dead in, 10, 16–
        17
    transcendental environment as perception
        in, 11, 19, 27, 38, 44–46, 51, 54; *see
        also* transcendental NDEs
    see also surgical experiences
counseling:
    for dying patients, 144–145
    in post-NDE period, 137–139

death:
    awareness of, 16–18, 162–163
    beliefs about, 166–168
    as "big secret," 15, 23, 186
    clinical vs. biological, 8–9, 185
    expectations about, 166–168
    fear of, *see* death anxiety
    individual's prediction of, 145–147
    nonphysical causes of, 147–148
    psychological component of, 145–150
death anxiety, 212, 213
    doctor-patient relationship and, 139–143
    NDE in reduction of, 6, 12–13, 60–61,
        125–126, 143, 145
    in physicians, 139–140
defibrillation in resuscitation, 58

déjà vu phenomenon, NDE vs., 45
delusions, drug-induced, NDEs as, 168–171
demographic background of NDE study
    subjects, 6, 11, 57–60, 185, 189–193,
    207–208
depersonalization, NDE and, 160–163
Dickstein death anxiety scale, 13, 61
dreams, NDEs as, 165–166
drugs, used in medical crises, 10, 58, 91,
    168–171
dying:
    as choice, 23, 26, 47, 48, 49, 50–52, 124,
        126, 145–147, 148–150
    point of no return in, 51, 147
    unidentified force in return from, 51
dying patient:
    counseling for, 144–145
    hospices for, 144
    medical care system and, 137, 140–145
    medical training related to, 142–143
    negative death image as confronted by,
        140, 142
    premonitions by, 145–147

EEG, "flat," 8
ego survival, NDE and, 159–160, 161, 166
Einstein, Albert, 186
Emory University School of Medicine, 13
endorphin release, effect of, NDE vs., 171–
    173
epileptogenic discharges, NDE vs., 173–
    174, 182
"extrapsychic" perception, 181

fabrications, NDEs as, 156–160, 184, 185
fantasies about death, 152, 166–168, 179
Florida, University of, 1, 3, 7, 133
    Medical Grand Rounds on Near Death
        Experiences at, 153
Freud, Sigmund, 159, 160, 161, 166
fright, in NDE, 10, 20, 40, 41–43, 53

Gainesville Veterans Administration Hospi-
    tal, 52
Garfield, Charles, 184n
Greyson, Bruce, 184n
guilt feelings, in NDE, 138

Haggard, H. W., 175–176
hallucinations, autoscopic, NDEs vs., 10,
    134, 164–165, 168–171, 173–174
happiness, in NDE, 19, 20, 33, 34, 47
Henderson, Y., 175–176
hexing, psychic death, and, 147
home locale, of NDE study subjects, 158
hospices, 144
hypercarbia, 176–178

hypnotic regression, evidence obtained from,
    80, 154
hypoxia, 152, 175–176

information supplied to patients, as expla-
    nation of NDE, 114
International Association for Near-Death
    Studies, 184n
intuition, in prediction of time of death,
    145–147

Johns Hopkins University, 148
*Journal of the American Medical Associa-
    tion (JAMA)*, 79–80, 152

Kastenbaum, Robert, 151
Kreutziger, Sarah, 3–4
    in NDE study, 5, 13, 156
Kübler-Ross, Elisabeth, 144

Laetrile, 141–142
Lancet, 146, 171
"learning" of out-of-body abilities, 116–123
Life After Life (Moody), 3–5, 6, 10, 55, 77,
    133, 156, 173
    medical community's response to, 151–
        152
*Life at Death: A Scientific Investigation of
    the Near Death Experience* (Ring),
    184n
life enhancement, due to NDE, 126–127
location of "crisis" event," in research anal-
    ysis, 58, 59, 60
loneliness, in NDE, 20
Ludwig, Arnold, 174–175
Lukianowicz, A., 164
Lundahl, Craig, 184n

McFarland, R. A., 176
"mechanism of death," 146–148
media, NDE exploited by, 151–152, 158
medical care system:
    altered views on abnormal psychiatric
        processes in, 134–137, 139
    attitude of professionals toward death in,
        140, 142
    doctor-patient relationship in, 137–141
    implications of NDE on, 133–143
    physicians' attitude toward death in, 139–
        140
    post-resuscitation anxiety and, 137–139
    sensitivity toward "unconscious" patients
        in, 133–134
medications:
    as inhibitors of NDE, 170–171
    research analysis of, 58, 91, 168–171
Meduna, L. J., 176–178

method of resuscitation, in research analysis, 58, 59, 60, 83–115, 196–200
mind-brain dualism, 181–184, 185
Moody, Raymond, 3–5, 6, 10, 55, 77, 133, 156, 173
morphine, 168, 171
mourning grief, after NDE, 128–129
Mystery of the Mind, The (Penfield), 183

narcotics, NDE and, 58, 91, 168–171
near-death experience (NDE):
acceptance of life and death after, 126, 145, 157
acceptance of pain and ordeals after, 128, 157
brain functioning and, 171–178
circumstances of, 56, 58, 60, 196–200, 203
conscious fabrications as explanation of, 156–159
content in, *see* content of NDEs
"crisis event" and, 7, 11, 152
criticism and alternate explanations of, 83–115, 153, 178, 184
death of loved ones as seen after, 128
detached feelings in, 17–18, 21, 25, 27, 28, 29, 31, 32, 35, 42, 159, 169, 184
drug-induced states of consciousness vs., 10, 168–171
effect on subjects' lives of, 124–133, 145, 148–149, 157
feelings predominating in, 10, 18–20, 21, 23, 29, 40, 41, 76, 78, 145, 148–150, 174
frequency of, 56–57
Freudian explanations of, 159, 160, 161, 166
general characteristics of, 14–23
guilt feelings in, 138
ineffability of, 15, 19, 23
international forum on, 184*n*
medical care system and, 124, 133–143
mind-brain split and, 181–184, 185
as "mind trip" fad, 151–152
multiple occurrences of, 16*n*, 56, 57, 159–160
as "non-ordinary mode of perception," 144
out-of-body hypothesis about, 184–185
patterns in, 5, 27, 31, 32, 33, 34, 36, 41, 47, 48, 49, 50, 52, 158, 160, 178
pleasant feelings in, 18–19, 20, 21, 23, 26, 29, 31, 33, 34, 40, 41, 43, 44–46, 47, 148–150, 155, 171–172
predispositions of subjects and, 57–58, 118, 166–168
previous knowledge of the NDE and, 57–58, 158, 189–193

professional recognition required for, 133
psychiatric basis ascribed to, 134–137, 139, 164–165
psychological factor in survival during, 145–150
psychological near-death experiences vs., 161–162, 163
religious views strengthened by, 129, 132
reluctance to return in, 18, 21, 33, 52, 145, 148–150
semiconscious state distinguishable from, 155–156
sense of death in, 16–18, 162–163
sense of reality in, 16, 22–23, 157, 165–166, 170
"separated self" as seen in, 10, 21–22, 23, 25, 27, 34, 183–184; *see also* autoscopic NDEs; out-of-body experiences
study approach to, *see* research studies
subconscious fabrication as explanation of, 159–160
surgical complications and, 56, 63–80
ten elements examined in, 10–11, 59
theoretical (conceptual) framework for, 181–184
thought processes in, 22, 169, 172, 176
timelessness in, 15–16, 23
types of, 27, 41, 52, 204–205
vocational choices made after, 132
voluntary recurrences of, 116–123
unpleasant feelings in, 10, 19–20, 40, 41–43, 53
see also autoscopic NDEs; autoscopic surgical experiences; combined NDEs; surgical experiences; transcendental NDEs; transcendental surgical experiences
Negovskii, Professor, 8, 185
New England Journal of Medicine, 141
Noyes, Russell, 161–162, 163, 184n

Oakes, Annalee, 184*n*
"On Awakening Paralyzed During Surgery—A Syndrome of Traumatic Neurosis" (Blacher), 79–80
On Death and Dying (Kübler-Ross), 143–144
out-of-body experiences, 16, 19, 20–22, 23, 34, 45, 47, 50, 53, 183–184
autoscopic NDEs vs., 27
detached elevated position in, 17–18, 21, 25, 27, 28, 29, 31, 32, 35, 42, 169, 184
as "learned" phenomenon, 118–123
scientific assumptions and, 181, 185
sensationalizing of, 151–152
subject's ability to describe, 6
in surgical procedures, 64–67, 69–70, 72–73, 74–75

pain, post-NDE acceptance of, 128
painlessness, in NDE, 18–19, 31, 149, 155,
  171–172
"peak" event, NDE as, 124–125
Penfield, Wilder, 173–174, 182–183
personal relationships, post-NDE view of,
  132
pharmacological effects, NDE vs., 168–171
Philips, John Hunter, 146
"Physicians Consider Death" (Feifel, Hanson, Jones, and Edwards), 140
powerfulness, feelings of, in NDE, 34
"Predilection to Death" (Weisman and
  Hackett), 146
presences in transcendental NDEs, 47, 49,
  210–211
primitive peoples, psychic death among,
  146, 147
prior knowledge:
  of CPR techniques by NDE study sub-
    jects, evaluation of, 83–115, 195
  of model NDE stories, 158
psychiatric disorders, NDE vs., 134–137,
  139, 164–165
psychical seizures, 173–174
"psychic death," 146–150
  in battlefield conditions, 147–148
  in laboratory animals, 148
  among primitive peoples, 146, 147
psychological component to death, 145–150
psychological factors, NDE and, 159, 160–
  163, 166
psychological near-death experiences,
  Noyes's report on, 161–162, 163
publicity on NDEs, 57–58, 151–152

reality, sense of, in NDE, 16, 22–23, 157,
  165–166, 170
religious beliefs, 2
  NDE and, 40, 44, 45, 46, 47, 48, 49–50,
    54, 76–77, 129–132, 180, 185–186,
    189–193
research studies:
  analysis of data in, 55–62
  animal experiments in, 148
  by anthropologists, 147–148
  author's scepticism at outset of, 157, 158
  on brain functioning, 171–178
  categories of medical conditions in, 56,
    58, 60, 196–200
  content vs. background compared in, 59–60
  continued work in, 184
  control studies in, 84–86, 87, 113–114
  "crisis event" defined for, 7
  critical evaluation of NDE in, 83–115,
    153–178
  death anxiety scales used in, 13, 61
  further questions for, 185

interviewing methods in, 9–12, 156, 189–
  193
investigators' background and qualifica-
  tions in, 5, 13
medical records examined in, 26–27, 37,
  40–41, 54, 57n, 58, 67–68, 71, 73–74,
  77, 78, 90–91, 93–94, 98, 103, 109–
  110, 112, 153
on medications, 58, 91, 168–171
Moody's work and, 4–5, 6, 10, 55, 56,
  57, 60
objectives of, 5–7, 10, 55
personal recollections as source in, 9–12,
  58
potential uses for, 143–145
prior general knowledge evaluated in,
  83–87, 195
prospective study in, 6, 12, 56, 194, 202
prospective vs. referred cases in, 12, 56
recording of interviews in, 10, 12
statistical methods in, 187–188
study dates of, 12, 13
subjects in, 5, 7, 9, 12, 57–60, 158, 163,
  189–193, 207–208
terminology used in, 7–9, 152–153
timing of interviews in, 11–12, 57, 60, 84
variables considered in, 58–59
Richter, Curt, 148
Ring, Kenneth, 184n
Rocky Mountain Medical Journal, 80

sadness, in NDE, 19–20
scenic beauty of transcendental environment, 43, 44–46
Schnaper, Nathan, 166, 174, 175
Schoonmaker, Fred, 184n
scientific method, 2
  scientific belief vs. scientific data and,
    152, 179–184
semiconscious perceptions, as explanation of
  NDE, 115, 153–156
sensationalism, associated with NDE, 151–
  152
Sherrington, Sir Charles, 181–182
social background of NDE subjects, 6, 11,
  57–60, 189–193, 207–208
soul, NDE and, 25, 181, 185
*Soul Hovering Over the Body Reluctantly
  Parting with Life, The* (Blake), 25
spirits in transcendental NDEs, 11, 22, 23,
  44, 46–50, 210–211
  communication with, 47–52
  content of communication with, 47, 210–
    211
  happiness and tranquility of, 47, 48, 50
  method of communication with, 47
  "return" influenced by, 50–52, 54
  visually perceived, 48–50, 51

Stevenson, Ian, 184*n*
Stokes-Adams syndrome, NDE after, 162
support measures in resuscitation, in research analysis, 58, 196–200
surgical experiences, 56, 63–80
autoscopic aspects of, 64–75
circumstances of, 201
near-death crisis event vs., 63
other investigators' reports on patients'
awareness in, 79–80
transcendental aspects of, 75–80

telepathy, in transcendental NDEs, 47
Templer death anxiety scale, 13, 61
temporal lobe seizure, NDE vs., 173–174
thanatology, 142–145
NDE and, 143–145
recent changes in, 144
thinking, clarity of, in NDE, 22, 169, 172,
176
Thomas, Lewis, 146–147, 171
"thought travel" in NDEs, 33–34
"To Sleep, Perchance to Dream . . ."
(Blacher), 152, 162
tranquility, feelings of:
in NDE, 18–19, 21, 29, 40, 41, 145,
148–150
in transcendental surgical experiences,
76, 78
transcendental NDEs, 11, 19, 27, 38, 39–
54, 56
author's hypothesis about, 185
autoscopic elements combined with, 42–
43, 52–54, 185
borders (limits) perceived in, 51
dark region (void) in, 41–43
difficulties in corroboration of, 185
ethereal scenes in, 46, 54, 209
life review and, 50
light in, 40, 42, 43–44
movement sensations in, 41–42, 43
religious content in, 40, 44, 45, 46, 47,
48, 49–50, 54
"return" in, 50–52, 54
scenic beauty perceived in, 43, 44–46
spirits or presences encountered in, 11,
22, 23, 44, 46–50, 210–211

transcendental surgical experiences, 75–80
Blacher's report and, 79–80
environments perceived in, 76
as identical to NDEs, 75
light perceived in, 78
medical account of procedure and, 77, 78
religious content of, 76–77
subjective sense of dying in, 76, 77, 78
tranquility, felt in, 76, 78

unconsciousness:
anesthesia and, 63
definition of, 7, 152–153
deincephalon and, 182
duration of, in research analysis, 58, 59,
60, 196–200
medical personnel's treatment of, 133–
134
mistaken assumption of, 153–154
sense of death and, 16, 56
in surgical situations, 63

visual perceptions in NDEs, 6, 10, 18, 19,
20, 21, 25–34, 53
critical evaluation in cardiac arrest cases
of, 83–115
details in, 28–31, 87–113, 158–159, 184
medication as inhibitor of, 170–171
nonspecific details in, 86–87
semiconscious state and, 154–156
in surgical procedures, 64–67, 69–70, 72–
73, 74–75, 80
in transcendental experiences, 48–50
witnesses' verification of, 36–37, 72, 75,
99, 112–113, 159, 184
vocational choices, post-NDE, 132
"Voodoo Death" (Cannon), 147

"will to live," NDE and, 124, 126, 145–
150
witchcraft, psychic death and, 147
witnesses:
autoscopic experiences verified by, 36–37,
72, 75, 99, 112–113, 159, 184
in surgeon-patient comparisons of surgical procedures, 68–69, 71
transcendental surgical experiences and,
77, 78

About the Author

Dr. MICHAEL B. SABOM is an Assistant Professor of Medicine, Division of Cardiology, at Emory University and a staff physician at the Atlanta VA Medical Center. He received a B.A. degree from Colorado College and an M.D. degree with honors from the University of Texas Medical Branch in Galveston. Board certified in both Internal Medicine and Cardiology, Dr. Sabom is a member of Phi Beta Kappa, a Fellow of the American College of Cardiology, and a Fellow on the Council of Clinical Cardiology of the American Heart Association. He has contributed more than a score of articles dealing with cardiology and the near-death experience to professional journals and textbooks. He has also lectured widely on the topic of the near-death experience and has appeared on many national television programs. Dr. Sabom lives with his wife and son in Decatur, Georgia.